River Stories

River Stories

Growing Up on the Wisconsin

Stories about Dace Chamberlain

By Delores Chamberlain
and his children

PRAIRIE OAK PRESS
Madison, Wisconsin

Prairie Oak Press
821 Prospect Place
Madison, Wisconsin 53703

Typeset by Quick Quality Press, Madison, Wisconsin
Printed in the United States of America
by Sheridan Books, Chelsea, Michigan

Library of Congress Cataloging-in-Publication Data

Chamberlain, Delores.
 River Stories : growing up on the Wisconsin : stories about Dace Chamberlain / by Delores Chamberlain and his children.—1st ed.
    p.   cm.
ISBN 1-879483-70-X
 1. Chamberlain, Dace—Juvenile literature. 2. Wisconsin—
Biography—Juvenile literature. [1. Chamberlain, Dace. 2. River life—Wisconsin. 3. Wisconsin—Biography.] I. Title.

CT275.C4537 C48 2000
977.5'043—dc21   00-047828

This book is dedicated to the life and memory of James Chamberlain, Jr., who was known to his family and his close friends as Dace. A poem called "The Oak Willow Man," written about Dace by the poet Al Blank, captures the spirit and essence of this average man who had exceptional and unique qualities as a father. It is a recognition of both his oak-like strength and his human weaknesses.

In the lives of those who loved him, the loss of this man has left a void that can never be filled. We make you this promise, Oak Willow Man. We will keep the memory of you fresh in our hearts and our minds, and we will pass all the wonderful stories about you on to your descendants.

—The Family

A note to my children, by Delores Chamberlain

This book is also dedicated to our children, who unselfishly made great sacrifices to come home and care for their dad during the last months of his life. Your love made it possible for him to move on with dignity, even in the face of great suffering. I would like for you to remember your father as an artist, a teacher, and a friend, as well as a parent. Through him, you learned many things that most people can only read about in adventure books.

He encouraged and respected your individuality and loved you each in different ways. Each of you contributed memories, poems, stories, or artwork to this book, or played a role in stories about Dad.

James Chamberlain III
Robin Chamberlain Transo
Rock Chamberlain
Peter Chamberlain (died in 1976)
Michael Chamberlain
Mark Chamberlain
Casey (Cassandra) Chamberlain
Francine Chamberlain (died in 1961)
Crink (Crystal) Chamberlain Hauck
Joseph (Joe) Chamberlain

Thank you, one and all.

Love,
Mom

Contents

Homage to the Oak Willow Man

By Al Blank

There is this man smooth as bark
(if contradiction can be tolerated)
who sits beside me. We share

some beer, some lies about fishing
and women, lies which make
his blue eyes shimmer with sly humor.
He throws out these baited lines
and waits, waits some more
until he hooks me with his truth,
his distilled dreams, his lusts
for all things natural—
bad natural, good natural, dark or light
natural—hell, just Man natural, you know?

Into the woods, to the river.
This is home beyond home.
He tramps his own trail into the deep,
towards the river, rubbing his hide
against a tree, deer-like:
a perpetual rutting moves
this man to join with all living forces.

To be sure, he knows well
the oak and willow,
true trees which accept a slanted truth
for the sapling does not always
grow straight but allows
there can be character in twisted bendings.

Out of the wood, the river flows.

Special thanks to Fr. John Urban for the loving care that he gave to the family during both difficult and happy times.

Thanks to Alice Loew and Tom Strobel for the illustrations they provided, and to Robin Chamberlain Transo and Joe Chamberlain, for their artwork.

To the poet and educator, Al Blank, who has been a great friend and a source of encouragement over the years, we all thank you for your friendship to Dace and to your dedication to the family. We shall always be grateful.

Thanks to Brianne Togstad Schwarz for listening so intently to Dace's tall stories, and to her parents, Mary Togstad and Jerry Schwarz, for providing the photo that appears on the cover of this book. It captures a precious moment between Dace and Brianne.

Preface

THESE ARE THE recollections of a father as seen through the eyes of his children. They tell a story about his youth as well as their own, and take the reader on nature adventures that they shared with him from early childhood into their adult lives.

This book is a compilation of stories about a man who taught his family to survive and thrive on the lower Wisconsin River and its backwaters. Dace Chamberlain taught his children to respect the river and its swamps and marshes, and always to protect the fish and wildlife that gave them life.

Today, when often it seems that the father's role in the family is minimized, these stories show that a father need not have wealth or position to be a good father, or to form strong and lasting bonds with his children and to instill in them a sound sense of values.

River Stories speaks of the joys that these children derived from all their many shared family experiences, from making maple syrup in the backyard (which sometimes meant collecting sap with a boat during high water) to a first deer hunt, or to a rare experience in saving a skunk from drowning during high water.

It also reveals the dangers of living on the riverfront with a large family of small children. There is the story of a harrowing escape during a deadly October rise in the river, and a time when an unexpected ice jam on the river brought a real threat to life. Their lives would not have been spared had it not been for the young husband and father, Dace Chamberlain, who fought the rampaging river to save them.

It is a book about the relationships between a father and his children, about the many river lessons that they learned from him. In this book, they share many memories: How their father taught them to trap and to care for the furs, how to hunt deer and field-dress their game, about fishing and spearing and how to smoke fish and meat. Dace Chamberlain taught them how to build boats, how to read the signs of the river for safe travel, and how to survive in the wilderness.

River Stories tells of how this father delighted his children with toy balloon races in the backwaters of the Wisconsin River, and how he led them to a pirate's stash of buried treasure (handmade and planted) on Feather Island. The "treasure" never would have been discovered, had not the children found a map that Dace secretly tucked into an old book which he then asked them to read.

This was a man with an outstanding sense of humor and delight about him. He shared his curiosity and wonderment about how things worked. One of his children recalls the time Dad made a machine that would turn out a new rope as fast as he could turn the handle on the homemade contraption. Helping Dad make rope was among that son's favorite memories.

Dace appreciated beauty and art in nature, whether it was in an agate that he found and polished just to carry in his pocket and show to his children, or carving a willow whistle that they could play a tune on, or even, while hunting, to watch a deer run past him during a gentle snowfall.

He taught his children how to build a cabin from discarded scraps of lumber, and how to design and build a flat-bottom wooden boat that was the best fishing boat on the river. His children learned how he cleared the land and why he was forced to move his growing family into a dangerous area.

We also learn that, at times when there was a need for food on the table for his large family, certain fishing, hunting, or trapping regulations were overlooked but never disrespected.

In recalling stories about their father, Dace's children reveal their feelings and their admiration and love for him, and for the many things he taught them.

This is a story also about a man who fought and won a hard battle against alcoholism, a disease that so often afflicts fathers of large, poor families. The story mentions this aspect of his tribulations but does not go into great detail about his inner struggles, other than to mention that he endured them.

The book is a positive account of Dace Chamberlain's life as seen through the eyes of his children and was written with them as a way of coping with the grief that resulted from his death, caused by leukemia.

Finally, it is a book about growing up on the river during the 1950s and '60s, about survival under the most severe of circumstances, and about how a family turned a difficult experience into a wonderful adventure.

CHAPTER ONE

Home Ground

THE WISCONSIN RIVER was his front yard, and he knew all of her secrets. He knew every square inch of the river bottoms and he felt at home there.

When he was a young boy in school, he'd slip away from football practice and go home and get his fishing pole and head for the river. When the fish weren't biting, he'd take his 12-gauge shotgun and go hunting in the woods and swamps, which stretched out from behind his home for miles to the riverbank.

He'd take birdshot with him, hoping to shoot at some mallard ducks or pheasants which were plentiful in the marshes or the high ground during the fall of the year. Sometimes he would take his .22 rifle with him and bring home several squirrels for his mother to fix for supper.

After high school, he went into the Army for a time, but how he missed his beloved swamps and woods that joined the river! He decided then that he would never go so far from home again, if it meant staying away for any length of time.

In the spring of the year, he would leave the house early in the morning so he could be there when the mallard ducks started their mating calls. The sound would be almost deafening because there were so many of them. Their calls were "the music of nature" to him. This was not the time for hunting. It was the time for listening. He would spend hours there, until the sun came high enough in the sky to quiet the mallards for the day.

This was his home ground, so it was no surprise to anyone when he decided to build a cabin on the river's edge. He didn't want it to be anything fancy, just a place to go and fix a pot of bean soup and coffee and swap fishing or hunting stories with his river cronies. The main purpose of the cabin was to provide a warming house for him and fellow deer hunters who came here in late November to hunt the bottoms and the many small islands that are sprinkled up and down the river.

The river's edge was the perfect place, he thought, because he could tie up his boat in front of the cabin and it would be close at hand when he wanted to get over to the islands where the deer would go, when the activity on the main bank got too much for them during deer season.

Dace Chamberlain had but few dreams at this stage in his life. He planned to follow in his father's footsteps and move houses. A cabin on the river was the only dream that he really focused on when he was twenty years old. His hobbies were fishing, hunting, boating and trapping, and just enjoying the great outdoors.

If he had a cabin, he could pursue his hobbies and feel that he had some independence. "What a perfect place to sleep in the summer and listen to the water rushing all night long," he thought.

It was unclear who owned the land where he wanted to put his cabin. He knew that Milo Sitts owned land in that general area, and he also knew that the State of Wisconsin had an easement several hundred feet on both sides of the highway that led to the bridge. He hoped that the place where he wanted to build was not on State-owned land.

Mr. Sitts. informed him that the State easement was only nine hundred feet wide and that the site he liked was on Sitts' property and not on State property. He would not sell his land but he told Dace that he was welcome to build his cabin there. "You go ahead and build and keep an eye on things down there for me," Milo said. "I won't charge you anything and that way you won't have to pay any taxes on it."

Dace was grateful for Milo's generosity and decided to get to work building the cabin right away. He labored at night over sketches he would draw over and over again. "It had to have a screened-in porch wide enough for a bed and open enough to allow for a breeze to sweep across him on warm summer nights." He thought about lying in his bed and looking up at the stars, then drifting off to sleep in perfect bliss.

The first thing he had to do was decide how high off the ground the cabin should be. When the river "came up," the cabin had to be up high enough so that the water wouldn't flood it. He had studied the river for years and knew that flooding would happen several times a year.

The first rise came when the winter snows melted and the runoff filled the swamps. Then there was the dreaded June rise when the bottoms would all be flooded. Sometimes there was an October rise. He never was quite sure why that happened. He did speculate that the dams up the river were probably opened up to lower the water level above the dams. Usually the October rise didn't amount to much, unless there had been a wet summer.

He thought long and hard about the height of the cabin. One day while standing where he had planned to build, he was looking down the river. The site he liked was about a thousand feet from the seven-span bridge that crossed the river about a mile from Boscobel, the small town where he had grown up.

Suddenly he realized that no matter how high the water got, it never went as high as the bridge floor or over the road that led to the bridge. He had never remembered traffic being held up because of water. That was the answer to his question. He decided that the bottom of his cabin had to be as high as the bottom of the bridge.

He arranged to get some old highline poles that had been discarded. He got a transit, a shovel, and a saw, and started building his cabin according to his sketches.

Hole digging came first. Then he drove stakes into the ground and sited them with the transit to the bottom of the bridge. He marked the stakes. This is where he would cut off his poles once he had them set into the holes in the ground and held firm with a cement base. He wanted the structure to be strong, so he put in twelve base poles. The cabin would be about eight feet off the ground.

The one-room cabin would be 12 x 14 feet in addition to an 8 x 14-foot porch. "That would be wide enough for a bed and some chairs, besides," he thought. He wanted to be able to invite his brothers down and have them all sit around and look out at the river together and just talk.

His brothers had taken Dace with them to the river since he was a small boy and shared their love for nature with him. He had a great admiration for his three brothers. He never referred to them by their names without saying brother first. Brother Harold, Brother Buzz, and Brother Paulie was what he always called them, even to strangers. How he loved just sitting around with them, swapping stories. As I recall, it was hard to tell which one was the biggest prevaricator. Stories rolled off their lips one after another and usually only a small part would be based on fact. Then how they all would laugh at the other's story.

Dace formed a frame for a floor by mounting 2 x 12-inch planks near the top of the poles. When he completed this, he began laying down a sub floor. The work was going well for him and the sound of his hammer pounding in the nails made him feel good.

He tore down what remained of an old log house on his grand-mother's farm and used the floorboards from the log cabin for the sub floor in his cabin. Next he laid a second floor. All that he had for the second floor was a pile of old boards that had been wainscotting in his grandmother's kitchen. The boards were only about three feet long and still had a light blue color from paint that was applied more than thirty years before. He would have bought what he needed from the local lumberyard, but boards cost money and he wasn't planning to invest much in the building.

By the time he finished laying down the second floor, he was so excited that one would have thought he had finished the whole cabin. He couldn't wait to complete the project, to begin sleeping down at the river, so he got an old mattress and several heavy quilts and carried them up his two-by-four ladder and put them on top of the platform that sat eight feet above the ground.

It was still cold at night when he first started staying at the river. Later, when it warmed up, there he would be, sitting on his platform almost every evening with a camp light burning dim in his lantern, drinking a can of Pabst beer and soaking up the sounds of the night. The bullfrogs in the backwaters, the hoot owls that lived in the trees in the upper bottoms, or Canadian geese honking and fish splashing the water as they jumped for insects.

Of course this symphony was backed up by the sound of rushing water from the main current of the river that flowed down past the banks just in front of the cabin site. He'd lie there on his mattress looking up at the stars and drift off to sleep with his nature sounds all around him. The joy that he felt was unmatched. This, to him, was the good life.

As the spring moved into summer, the mosquito population increased and soon there were too many for comfortable outdoor sleeping. The mosquitoes did motivate him to get busy and find more boards so he could go on with the construction of his little cabin. He just wasn't too willing to give up all of this because of a heavy mosquito crop.

He began an intense search for an old building that he could tear down and salvage enough lumber so he could go on with his work.

Many of his river cronies were excited about his cabin. They knew that they would be included in the cups of hot coffee and the bowls of hot bean soup or chili when the cold November winds chilled them during the deer hunt or the winter trap line. The thought of setting around a hot wood stove with a bunch of men always appeals to the pioneer spirit of outdoorsmen.

Now, all of a sudden, he wasn't alone in his search for more lumber. It seemed that each of them knew someone who had an old shed or a pile of unused lumber that they wanted to get rid of. Several of the men even helped tear down old outbuildings and pull the nails from the boards.

One man knew someone who had a pile of used gray brick siding that they had planned to haul to the dump but just hadn't gotten around to doing it. Some of the siding was in good shape and he happily accepted it to haul away.

The summer months were busy for him. He went to the river every day after work and worked on his cabin as long as there was light enough to see the nail he was pounding. Sometimes he would even work by his car's headlights to finish a section. How he hated to quit for the day when he could no longer see to work.

First the framework for the sides of the cabin went up, then the frame of the roof. After the outside wall boards were attached, he worked on the roof section and watched his dream becoming a reality. Next he sorted the gray siding and used only the best pieces. Matching the siding became quite a job, since some of it had been damaged along the edges. He wanted his cabin to look nice, so he would cut sections to match what he had already put up. When all of the siding was on, he put a couple layers of tarpaper on the roof and nailed lath across it to hold it in place. He began to believe that sitting around the fire might be something he would do that year.

Summer was ending and he wanted to get the wallboard and screens up in time for deer hunting. He wanted to insulate the cabin but didn't see it as really necessary, and it would be expensive. He worked late into the fall putting the finishing touches on his cabin to make it ready.

The nightclub owner from across the river had given him two big windows, and it didn't take him long to get them into place. Each window contained nine panes of glass, in three rows. He removed one of the panes and put an aluminum sheet in the opening, after cutting a stovepipe-size hole in the sheet. He put a stovepipe out through the hole with an elbow far enough from the outside wall that the hot pipe wouldn't cause a fire and burn down the cabin. He then ran the pipe several feet above the roof, braced it well with metal rods, and put a tin shield on top of the stovepipe. This would allow for the smoke to go out but would keep the sparks contained so that they wouldn't start the tarpaper roof on fire. He decided that his makeshift chimney would have to do until spring.

The nights were getting cold and the wind howled all around and under his cabin. He got an old sofa that opened out into a bed and put it inside the cabin. That would be his bed if he stayed there on winter nights. He'd think about porch sleeping next spring when it warmed up again. He got a few chairs and set them around the old wood stove. The top of the stove was flat and just big enough for a coffee pot and an iron kettle for soup making.

He cut up wood from fallen trees that were near the cabin and stacked it up on the porch so it would be dry when he needed it for a fire in the old stove. Everything was ready. The time had come for fishing and hunting stories to begin.

Even though people called him the River Rat, he was not the only one known by that name. Many other men who knew the river and the area around it were known by that name as well.

River Rat was a good name for Dace, however, because he had scurried around every tree and bush in the bottoms and he knew where every mink and otter run was, and where every fox den and muskrat house was. He knew the look of the water. If there was a snag somewhere below the surface or a hidden sandbar, he knew it. He knew the deer runs and their habits and he knew each and every gut that ran back from the river to the swamps, and he knew where all the best fishing holes were for miles up and down the river.

Throughout his life he was always considered an authority on all things pertaining to wildlife and nature, and certainly on anything to do with the river. The older he got, the more he was able to accomplish, according to some of the stories about him. He knew how to repair a gun, or design and build a boat, or fix just about anything anyone would have a problem with. Someone recalled once seeing him make a firing pin for a high powered rifle out of a spike nail. Someone else told about the time he made a bearing and an axle for an old car out of a piece of wood. They said it actually worked long enough for him to get the car from the river bottoms to a garage where he could get something better installed. There were always stories about his achievements. Most of them were true but some of them were a little hard to believe. He never admitted or denied the stories.

CHAPTER 2

A Temporary Home

It WOULD BE several years before he would spend his first full winter in the cabin. He hadn't gotten around to building the chimney or doing much of anything else in the way of improvements to the cabin, after the first year. He had been busy at other things. Dace and I got married and started a family.

We had been going together since he was nineteen and I was fifteen. His work with his father did not provide him with enough of an income to support us, so he went to work with a construction company that built roads and streets.

His work took us and our growing family away from his beloved town and river during the summer months. In the late fall, though, he always came back in time for deer hunting. During the winter months he had a trap line that led him on an eight-mile trek through the bottoms and along the river every morning. The furs he trapped brought an extra income that helped sustain the family.

Moving into the cabin was an exciting time for us and our three small children. It was also a time of desperation for a place to live. A few months prior to the move, our mobile home had burned and all our belongings were lost. After the fire, we had been living in a dismal basement apartment. Even though the cabin would be crowded with five people, it promised to be a nice change from the basement apartment, but it was also meant to be a temporary home until we could find something better.

The idea was to move into the cabin and rough it through the summer, then find something else before it got too cold. There was no electricity when we moved in, and there was no source of drinking water, not even an outdoor toilet.

The first priority was to get a well drilled and install a hand pump. Dace built a good-sized pump porch off the main porch and a set of steps from the ground up to the pump porch. He built a large landing halfway up the stairs so that he could tie a boat to the landing when the water rose.

He bought pipes and a sand point and he and a friend, Ralph Guist, drove the sand point down into the dirt and then down through the wet sand. They ran into water a few feet below the surface because the water level was the same as the river level. This water would have been all right for bathing, washing clothes, and watering the garden, but it was not fit to drink. The point was driven down forty feet further. The water at that level tasted alright but required testing to make sure it was safe to drink.

Someone gave Dace an old school outhouse and he moved it in on his father's house-moving truck. He dug a hole at the far end of the cabin site and mounted the outhouse over the hole. At last, life would take on a sense of normality, albeit primitive and unique.

The field mice found a new source of nest-making material whenever the roll of toilet paper was left out of the three-pound coffee can that was used to keep it dry.

Ironically, this was to be one of the last buildings that he would ever move. He never had an opportunity to return to the work that he wanted to spend his life doing.

A quiet solitude settled over the little home on the river as the spring got warmer, and it seemed as if we had a real home again. That year Dace had to drive back and forth to Madison every day for work with the construction company. Since we no longer had the mobile home, he was unable to take the family with him. Before he could make any change in the living arrangements, spring became summer and soon late fall was upon us once again.

There were no houses in town for rent, so we decided to stay at the cabin for the winter. Before the winter months had hardly begun, he was sorry that he had not insulated the building at the beginning. He realized that some critical modifications would have to be made when he and the family woke up on a twenty-degree-below-zero winter morning and found that the bedding was frozen to the wall.

The stove didn't provide enough heat for the night and the condensation from our breathing caused the walls to get wet and freeze. The wind howled all night around the corners, and under the cabin. The little building groaned at times with the cold. While we were in our beds we were warm, but Dace had to get up and stoke the fire and add chunks of wood throughout the night. If he slept too soundly and the fire went out, as it did sometimes, he would have to get up early in the morning and start it again to warm the room and dry out the moisture that seemed to be everywhere. The inside of the windows would be completely frosted over and the pail of drinking water would be one big chunk of ice. I would have to thaw the ice on the stove before making him his morning cup of coffee or make corn mush for the little ones.

The floor always stayed cold even after he went under the house and insulated the underside of the floor between the many 2 x 12 rafters. The children couldn't play on the floor during the real cold weather. When they wanted to sit down to play, I put them on the big bed.

A new baby was born that winter, right during the worst of the cold weather. He was named Peter. Now there were six of us in these tiny quarters.

The burden of his family living like this began to weigh heavily upon Dace, yet there was little he could do about it because of the lack of money to improve the current place, and the lack of affordable housing in town.

Salaries were terrible for the working man, only about $1.50 an hour. During winter months, unemployment compensation was the only source of reliable income and that was only about $38.00 a week. Trapping furs did supplement the family income some, but it was not dependable.

The family was too big to impose upon aging parents, and besides, we didn't want to move into someone else's home with children, no matter how rough things were.

There was a great deal of happiness and sharing among the family members, despite the close quarters and the hardships. The little cabin was actually fairly cozy most of the time.

In the evenings, we shared stories by lamplight. We discovered new wall shadow figures almost every night, along with the old favorites such as the dog and the rabbit, and the hawk, which would fly above the children's heads. They would hold up the little shadow puppets that Dace had made for them from blocks of wood. We all took part in the shadow puppet theater.

Dace always got to be the scary shadow puppet, which delighted the children. Sometimes he brought out a wooden "boogie man" or a troll, or a monster of some kind that he had made that day just to surprise them. If they did become a little frightened, he would immediately stop and show them the shadow puppet, and that he was only playing tricks. Then we would all laugh and start again.

During the day, while setting on the big bed, I would tell the children stories and draw illustrations for the stories as I told them. They especially liked the pictures I would draw showing them riding shiny new tricycles around the yard outside. Dace and I wanted desperately for them to have a big new tricycle to ride when spring came, but we knew there wouldn't be money for anything so lavish, and so I drew pictures of each of them riding on new tricycles. Each one of them had their own trike in the drawings and it was their favorite color. It would have its own little license plate with their name on it and a big basket to hold their stuffed animal. There was a place in the back of each tricycle for someone to stand up and ride along behind. They had many tricycle adventures during those story times. Every day it would be something new and as exciting as the day before. Some adventures had to be repeated and drawn over and over again.

I told them other stories as well, such as "Little Red Riding Hood" and "The Three Pigs." My stories never ended like the ones in the books, though. The wolf never ate anyone. The woodsman never killed the wolf but instead just chased him away and then sat down and had a nice cup of hot tea with Grandma. Oh, there were consequences for the wolf's bad behavior. Sometimes it involved the little pigs getting the best of him and tying a rope around his leg and then to a table leg and making him do the dishes ever after, or until he learned his lesson or chewed his way out. That seemed like punishment enough for his trying to get them into the stew pot.

Many years after the children had grown, the family was talking about how they had "roughed it" that first year at the cabin. One of the children asked us how we could have bought all those big new tricycles when money was so scarce. What a reward that remark was for me, to know that they had not really missed out on having a new tricycle after all.

Dace knew that when spring came he would have to figure out a way to keep the place warmer if we were to spend another year on the river.

The first thing he promised himself was that he would build a chimney. The arrangement that he had was too dangerous. If a fire was going in the stove when the wind was blowing, sparks would fly out and land on the gray brick siding, which was little more than thick tarpaper. It certainly wasn't fire-resistant and neither was the tarpaper roofing. The guard he had put in the top of the stovepipe didn't work very well when there was a strong wind.

Spring did come, eventually, and so did the mallard ducks. The marshes were filled with them and their mating calls woke us in the early morning. We didn't need an alarm clock to be awakened during mating season. The sounds of nature helped us forget the rough winter we had spent just staying alive.

The first sign of spring brought new ideas on how to improve the cabin. After the new cement block chimney was built, Dace poured a cement floor around the base poles, sloped toward a drain. He had planned to use a sump pump to suck the water out when the river started to rise. He then built a cement block wall all around the bottom of the cabin, and then he sided the cabin down to the ground to keep out the winter wind. Even though he expected water problems as soon as the rise came, he knew that it would keep the cabin dry most of the year, and the extra room was worth the inconvenience.

He built inside stairs that led up to a trapdoor in the porch floor. He also put a door in front of the cabin at ground level for safety and for easy access in and out. During summer months the trapdoor to the lower floor was kept closed and the porch space was used as he had originally intended. Now, with a two-story cabin, there was twice as much space for the family.

He made other changes, as well. The long drives to Madison and back every day left little time for anything else and he decided to try to get a job closer to home. He was fortunate to get work at the local Borden plant. The salary was less than he earned for construction, but the savings in gasoline alone made up the difference.

The Borden factory made baby food and processed whey. They had materials that arrived in tall cardboard barrels. The round lids were about two feet in diameter and made of thick composition board, held in place with a metal strip. After the barrels were opened, the lids were discarded.

Dace immediately saw the value in the discarded lids. They were thick enough to provide some insulation and would make a unique siding if he overlapped them. The problem was that he could not drive a nail through them. He solved that problem by drilling three holes in each one of them with a brace and bit. Then he nailed them on, one by one, to the side of the cabin. He used long nails so that he could leave the gray siding intact, since that, too, would act as an insulation. It took him all summer to side the cabin. When he had finished, the children thought it looked just like the gingerbread house from a book of fairy tales. Some people said that the new siding looked like fish scales, which seemed to be in keeping with a cabin on the river. Dace painted the siding and the cement blocks brown and trimmed them in white.

Someone had given him a storefront awning, which he shortened and mounted over the front porch. He painted the heavy cloth awning brown and made it look brand new, as if it were designed especially for the cabin.

What a sight it was! The cabin looked as if he had spent a fortune on it. He moved the big wood stove downstairs so that now he could build a fire on winter nights to keep the floor of the cabin warm. He also put vents in the floor, letting the warm air flow up into the upstairs. He also installed small vents near the peak of the roof, making the winter moisture problem a thing of the past. Dace never intended to relive that first winter on the river.

He made many other improvements, including putting on new roofing over the tarpaper. He made himself a promise that when the weather started to get cold he would winterize the porch so that the winter winds wouldn't be so unfriendly in the future.

Late in October that year, the power company came down and put up poles that ran from the cabin down to the high lines on the side of Highway 61 near the bridge. Soon the electric wires were strung and Adolph Sime, a local electrician, came and installed a fuse box inside the cabin. Dace had already wired the cabin himself, so it was just a matter of having the electrician check out his work and hook the wires up to the fuse box. Now he knew the family would be warm that winter and the children wouldn't have to sit on the bed to play.

Dace was an avid reader but he had poor eyesight. He had been reading by lamplight for so long that he had forgotten how well he could see by an electric light.

He got rid of the old propane gas refrigerator and bought a good secondhand electric refrigerator and a used gas stove for cooking. Meal preparation became a pleasure, but the food never tasted as good as when it was fixed on the old wood stove.

Sometime later we bought a TV on the time payment plan, and Dace nailed an antenna onto the roof. All the improvements made the cabin on the river an acceptable temporary home for the family. It was still too small, and there were no modern conveniences, but he played with the idea of it becoming the family's permanent home some day.

After the cabin improvements had been made, Dace seemed to be at peace with himself again, at least for the time being. Soon he would be able to devote more time to what he loved to do—fishing, boating, hunting, and trapping.

CHAPTER THREE

Clearing the Land

SPRING BROUGHT THE dream of gardening, but there was no open space to plant anything. All the land around the cabin was filled with brush and hundreds of half-grown soft maple trees. The land in front of the cabin would have to be cleared if we were going to have a lawn. There was a nice area in the back for a garden but that was a mass of thicket and trees as well.

Out came the ax, saws, hatchets, shovels, and a chain. Before long there stood a huge pile of brush, twice as wide and half as high as the cabin itself. The whole area was nothing but stubble. It was hard to walk without tripping and falling down. One might impale himself if he fell, so watching our step was crucial. No children were permitted in the area for fear that they might fall and put out an eye or something worse.

It was important to remove the stubble before someone got hurt. That's where the chain came in. The small trees had been cut about six inches off the ground so that one end of the chain could be wrapped around it and then the other end was affixed to the bumper of the old car. The brush roots came up fairly easy, but the tree roots caused the wheels to spin and dig into the soft ground before they would budge. What a terrible, tedious job. It seemed like a half-day's work hardly made a dent in the mess.

A young nephew got a lot of practice on the standard shift of an old '37 Chevrolet by changing gears from reverse to low and back to reverse again. He was an expert at clutching by the time the yard and garden were cleared and ready to be worked up. It's a wonder that the transmission or clutch or something else didn't give out on the old car, but it was built well and not afraid of work, just like its owner.

When the area was finally cleared, it was time for an evening bonfire and a whole lot of Pabst beer. We roasted wieners and marshmallows, and anyone in town who saw the smoke, and came down to investigate, was invited to join in the fun of just sitting around the fire and admiring the new look the place had taken on.

Men concerned with the river bottoms catching on fire were the curious ones who showed up. Not one of them refused a good cold beer or a hotdog. In fact they were still there when the bonfire was not much more than a pile of ashes. A couple of them left just long enough to go across the bridge to the Manhattan Club and bring back more beer, just in case anyone got thirsty before the fire went out.

As the night progressed, some of the men picked up hatchets and cut more brush and threw it on the fire. The garden spot got bigger and bigger. The next day I had a big job picking up all those empty beer cans.

The Boat Landing

After the major part of the clearing was completed for the yard and garden, Dace decided to clear a section of the riverbank for a boat landing. The place that he chose was just to the side in the front of the cabin and a straight shot in from the road. He had always planned on building a boat landing in that very spot, and that is the main reason he chose this particular site for the cabin. It was the reason he had designed the road to come onto the cabin site where it did. He wanted to drive in, circle around, and back the boat trailer down into the water.

The river's main channel was a few feet out from the water's edge at that spot, and that made this the perfect place to slope the bank. He had spent many hard hours shoveling, digging, and measuring, to get the grade of the slope just right so that a trailer holding a boat could easily be backed into the water, and the incline would be gentle enough to allow the trailer to be pulled easily from the water.

Soon the landing was completed, and it was time for brothers Buzz, Paulie, and Harold to bring their boats and try it out. Dace didn't own a boat of his own yet, but his brother Buzz always let him use his. It was made of lightweight aluminum and was great for speeding up the river if you just wanted to look around, but Dace thought it was terrible for fishing. "It's too damn noisy," he would say. "You can't even sit in quiet backwater in that thing. It scares all the fish away. When the water slaps against the sides, it can be heard all over. No self-respecting fish would come within a mile of your line. The least little breeze or a ripple in the water and it makes that damn pounding noise."

Everyone listening to him wondered how Buzz got all the fish he caught, but no one said anything. Besides, we all knew he was looking for an excuse to start building his own "flat-bottomed wooden boat" that he was always saying he was going to build some day.

Boat Building

Out came paper and pencil. Dace began sketching, drawing, erasing, and calibrating. He decided his boat would be sixteen feet long, and three feet across in the back and taper to about two feet wide in the front.

The bottom would be made out of a good piece of quarter-inch plywood; one with no knot holes or imperfections. The sides were to be made of plywood as well, cut in a way to give a gentle rise to the boat from the center forward so that the front end sat off the ground about six inches. This was done to give the boat what he called "skip," meaning that it would skip across the water nicely without taking on water in the front.

He then put a one-by-four-inch strip of pine board around the outer top edge on both sides. He mounted oar locks on the boards, one on each side toward the center. The ends of the boat were made from pieces of two-by-twelve-inch pine plank. The back end was twelve inches high, with the front end board cut down to a width of six inches. He then put "ribs" about eighteen inches apart in the bottom of the boat from front to back. The ribs, which were only about an inch and a half high, not only made the boat stronger but provided a place for a removable walk, which he made out of slats.

After all the nailing was done, he lovingly sanded every square inch of it. And then he caulked all the seams with a fine bead of a durable caulking compound.

He painted the boat brown on the outside and maroon on the inside, with a durable floor and deck paint. He painted the oars maroon to match the inside of the boat. The colors were perfect together. After the paint was dry, out came the stencil.

It was time for naming his little boat. Everyone knew he would choose something feminine, since he was a great fancier of women. His friends and family had been guessing for days and making all kinds of suggestions for the name. I thought it should be named *Red Onion*, after a boat we had taken shelter under during a storm when we were going together. One of the men thought he should name it *Marilyn Monroe* since it had such a nice shape.

The name was to go on the right front side. When he was ready to apply the letters, he made everyone stay back while he carefully worked. When he was done, he stood back to admire his work. "There, that's just right," he said. He had named it the *Robin Lynne*, after his little five-year-old daughter. The two older boys were a bit put out at first until he told them that boats aren't named after boys.

The boat was finished. Now all it needed was to be tested for leaks. There was great excitement as he and his friend Ralph carried the boat to the landing and eased it into the water. He explained to everyone before the launching that a boat needs to swell in the water for a while before making any judgments about it, so we should not despair if there was some seepage in places. He tied a length of new rope to an eye hook that he had mounted on the front and tied his new anchor to the other end. He pushed the boat out into the water and dropped the anchor on the ground. We all held our breath for the test. There had been no need to prepare us, because the little boat was water-worthy. It did not take on a drop of water.

Now came the acid test. How would she tread water? Dace mounted the five-horse Johnson outboard motor onto the stern. He had bought the motor at a sale and fixed it up. It was a small motor but it should have enough power to move her up river through the swift current, he thought. But he wasn't sure. It was time to see.

He started up the motor, put it in reverse, and moved out onto the river until he was well into the current. Then he went forward and up the river with Ralph sitting near the front. Ralph was a good-sized man, so if they didn't take on water going against the current it meant the design was right.

Up the river they went, then down the river going faster still, and waving at all of us on the bank like they had just seen us for the first time. There was no current to hold them back now and the little boat slipped along across the water with the grace of a bird in flight. Not a sound did she make. No slapping or banging was heard as the water flowed neatly by her sides. She was doing what came natural to her.

The *Robin Lynne* had been made with loving care and she was returning the love. They went below the bridge and turned. Back up the river they came, full speed, and pulled into the boat landing with big smiles on their faces. They hadn't taken on any water. The test was a success!

What a great feeling that must have been for Dace, standing there on his landing, in front of his cabin, looking at his own boat. After all those years of hard work, his dreams had finally become reality.

No sooner had their feet touched the ground when Ralph put in his order for a boat just like her. Later there were several others who came to ask Dace to design and build them a boat like the one he had built for himself.

CHAPTER FOUR

The Road In

THE ROAD TO the cabin from the main highway was always in terrible condition. It was little more than a trail through the woods at first, until Dace cleared the brush and trees along the sides of the trail. Every time it rained the road would be a muddy mess and the car was always getting stuck. After a wet spell it was necessary to park on the side of the highway and walk in, carrying groceries or whatever was needed at the time. To say the least, this was inconvenient.

Dace decided that the road needed a better base than the soft, black, forest soil. Driving in and out during good weather did not pack it down enough to make much difference when the rains came. He got an old box trailer and started hauling loads of shale and cinders from behind the Borden Plant where he worked. Every evening he would make at least five trips bringing the heaped-up loads of fill and spreading it on the road. On weekends he worked all day long, bringing more loads.

While he was at work, I would continue bringing loads of cinders throughout the day until it was time to pick him up from his job. What a chore that was for me, scooping the big shovels of cinders onto the trailer. The little ones would try to be patient as they waited in the car while I shoveled. It was especially hard on me, since I was with child. When I got enough on the trailer, I would drive the two miles back to the cabin road and shovel it off and return for another load. This continued all summer long. The road improved somewhat, but not enough to guarantee access all the time.

At the time, gravel cost about eight dollars for a five-yard load— a dump truck full. That was almost a full day's salary, so when we ordered a load of gravel, we spread it on the soft spots only.

When the weather warmed up and the river bottoms dried out, the road had more traffic than before. Word had spread about Dace's boat landing, so we began to have regular visitors. At first it was mostly his brothers and a few friends who brought their boats down on trailers and used the landing. What a simple procedure this was compared to the problems they had had in the past just getting their boats in and out of the river.

Each of Dace's family and his friends offered to put in loads of gravel to help improve the road. That made for further road improvement, and becoming stuck began to become a rarity. There were still weak spots in the road because it was so near to the marsh. No matter how much fill was put in, it always seemed that it just wasn't enough.

The blessing of the road improvement became a detriment when the members of several local rod-and-gun clubs descended upon the boat landing and acted as if it were public property.

Sometimes on a weekend as many as forty cars and trailers came down the cabin road to put their boats into the river. They would park their cars any and every place they could find, without any concern for the lawn or the garden. Many times, wives and children came along for a day of boating on the river.

Their lack of consideration was so great that at times it was necessary to ask them to get out of the garden. They even picked the flowers that we had planted. Privacy had become a thing of the past and our anger at their attitude was growing. They threw debris on the ground and played their radios without consideration for anyone who didn't care to hear their loud music. Kids were pulling radishes out of the garden and mothers came to the cabin to complain that we were out of toilet paper in the outhouse.

When we confronted them, some were rude, and once we were asked who the hell we thought we were. They treated us badly because we were poor and lived on the river, instead of in a regular house in town. To make things worse, the condition of the road began to deteriorate. After all the work we had done, to be treated this way was just too much to bear.

Dace approached the presidents of the different clubs and told them that they could continue using the road and the landing but that it would cost each boat owner a load of gravel, and that more consideration must be shown for our privacy.

The thought of having forty loads of gravel seemed like a dream come true to Dace. He knew he didn't need that much on the road itself, but now he planned to build a parking lot where trailers and cars could park and not be ruining the lawn and garden. He expected that the clubs would jump at the idea. How wrong he was. It angered the groups and they stomped off saying that they would build their own boat landing.

What a relief! Just like that they were gone. Wives, kids, trash, noise, snooping and all. Oh, there were a few who felt it was only fair that they help out, so they gave their eight dollars for gravel and we made them feel welcome to come and use the landing at any time. Privacy, for the most part, returned to the river bottoms once again. The people who continued to come down were usually respectful and enjoyable.

The road eventually improved enough so that Dace and his family could get in and out the year around, except for times of high water.

The rod-and-gun clubs went to the State and got money to build their boat landing. It cost the taxpayers a lot of money. The new public boat landing was poorly laid out and they had trouble with it for years. It had to be dredged out over and over again. It finally had to be redesigned, which did help, but there were still problems when the river level was low. Dace Chamberlain's landing, on the other hand, never needed dredging, and if the water level was low it meant that one would just have to back the trailer a little farther to reach water that was deep enough.

The public boat landing, situated just below the bridge, about 1,500 feet from Dace's landing, has an outhouse with toilet paper. It has trash containers and you can be fined if you throw your trash on the ground. It also has a public employee who comes around to maintain it.

The ironic thing about it is that many times when the water level is low, it is not uncommon to see people coming up the old cabin road pulling their boats. They may not know the history of how the public landing came into being, but they do know a place where they can get their boat into the river so that they can go fishing.

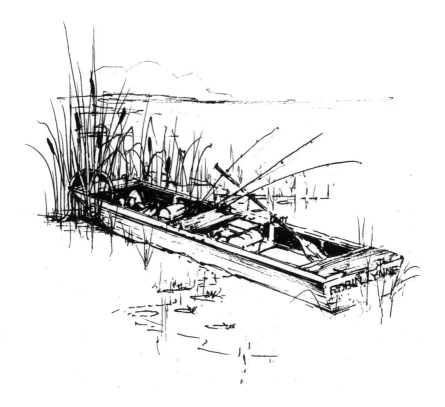

River Lessons

Dace's family was an important part of his life. He loved teaching them the joys of nature and how to survive and thrive under adverse conditions.

His hands were seldom idle. Even as he sat quietly with his children on the riverbank, fishing, he would have his jackknife out and be working on a small willow stick, showing them how to make a whistle.

He wanted them to fear and respect the river, but he also wanted them to enjoy it and know it the way he did. They were not allowed to be around the boat landing or go out in the boat unless they were wearing their life jackets. He started teaching them how to row a boat when they were six years old.

The children were fast learners but they weren't strong enough at first to manipulate the boat against the strong current. That took a long time to master, and long, hard hours at working the oars to make their little arms develop enough to even turn the boat around in the swift water. Dace was always right there, ready to grab the oars if necessary.

Jimmy, the oldest, was the most determined. After a few months of training every evening, he eventually was able to row across the main channel, over to Stumpy's Island and back without letting the boat go downstream even a few feet. That was a feat for a grown man. Often we would observe the fishermen start to row back from the island and wind up downstream thirty or forty feet from the boat landing. They would have to put all of their strength into rowing to move the boat against the current back up to the landing.

When they would see the six-year-old cross, they would ask him, "How do you do that?" He was always glad to let them know that the trick was to start out rowing upstream right away while they were still in quieter water, and keep doing that until they got to this side of the river. Sometimes Jimmy did so well that he had to let the boat float downstream a bit to come out at the landing.

"You're not starting to work against the current soon enough," he would tell them. "If you wait until you feel a pull, you are going to drift." He felt pretty proud of himself when men noticed how well he could row or when he could give them advice on how to cross the river against the current.

He began to recognize the signs of underwater snags and sandbars, and as time went on, Dace taught him how to spot shallow water at a distance. This was of great importance if he were to learn to run the outboard motor some day. When rowing, it is unlikely that one could hit anything hard enough to tip the boat over. About the only way that could be done is if the rower stood up and overbalanced it. A flat-bottom wooden boat is quite safe if you use good common sense when you are on the water. It isn't like a canoe. It's a navigation feat to keep a canoe afloat in swift water.

Operating an outboard motor is another matter. Because you are moving fast, you need to know the depth of the water ahead of you at all times. You also need to know what is under the water so that you don't hit something that may cause you to capsize. If you are going at a good pace and hit a sandbar or a snag or anything under the water such as a log or a branch, you could be badly hurt or even killed.

To operate an outboard on the Wisconsin River, you have to be able to know the look of the water all around you, and especially up ahead of you for a hundred feet or more. When someone says they can read the river, that is what they mean. They know what kind of water they are entering at all times before entering it.

Boating on the Wisconsin River is different from boating on any lake. The depth of the water is never the same from one day to the next, and it can be very deep and extremely shallow, just a few feet apart.

The Wisconsin River is always changing. That is probably why so many people refer to the river as a "she" or a "her." You hear them make statements such as, "She is high today," or, "the bottom went out of her last night," meaning the water level dropped fast. They speak of her like she was an ancient woman—temperamental, changeable, and dangerous, yet always very beautiful and demanding of respect from those who enjoy her.

CHAPTER SIX

The Skunk Flood Story

Robin Chamberlain Transo

Every year on the river the floods came at least twice. It was after an early spring flood when I was five years old that Dad took me out in his boat, the *Robin Lynne*. I loved going out on the river with Dad, despite the fact that I held a deep fear of, but respect for, the river itself.

The water was still up but you could walk on the soggy earth with rubber boots and avoid puddles. Dad wanted to see the damage the river had done to some of his favorite fishing holes, so we proceeded upriver to investigate.

It was at times like these that I was glad Dad knew the river. Just under us the untrained navigator might run into the countless unseen sandbars or trees washed away by the flood. Dad knew the channel and could read the water the way some people read the newspaper.

As we moved up river our hearts sank at the signs of destruction. The fishing holes were gone. The floodwaters had cut a whole new channel and filled in one of the old fishing holes with sand. The water was murky and brown and many trees were down along the banks.

Change is the only thing certain on the river, so we just swallowed and moved on upstream to see what else had changed. In many places the river willows were still under water; redwing blackbirds clinging tightly to the small trunks and branches, swinging back and forth and singing their lovely river songs. Dad slowed the boat down so we could hear their songs together.

Up around the bend, Dad turned the boat around for our return trip. I was mesmerized by the ripples under the boat and let my fingers run through the water. For just a second, a motion caught my attention out of the corner of my eye. I looked up and there we both saw him at the same time: a skunk swimming for his life. I couldn't believe it, but it had only enough strength to let out a little cry and then it went under. "Dad, you've got to help him!" I shouted. "We'll get sprayed!" was his reply, but as the little fellow came up for the second time Dad changed his mind and stuck his oar out and scooped him up. As he carefully put him into the boat, Dad warned me what could happen to us. He said Mom wouldn't let either of us in the cabin for a week. "We'll have to take a bath in tomato juice in Grandma's basement!" he warned.

I have never seen Dad row so quietly in his whole life. As for myself, I don't remember saying anything the whole trip down the river. I just sat there and looked at that poor water-logged skunk trying to get its breath. I know I almost lost mine when it stood up and shook off. I thought he looked so funny and wanted to laugh, but as soon as a giggle came spilling out of my lips, Dad's eyebrows scrunched together like he would burst if I made a sound.

So there we were, trapped like that for a good fifteen minutes, Dad with one eye on the river while he rowed and the other on that skunk, and me with both eyes on the skunk except for the occasional glance at Dad.

When we came in close to the boat landing, Dad came out with the plan. "When I say jump, you jump out of the boat and hightail it to the cabin!" he whispered. I nodded in agreement and when we landed the boat I did almost what he said. I didn't make it quite to the cabin before I turned around and saw the skunk walking down the boat's oar like a circus performer until he reached land. At that point, the skunk walked up to my Dad, who was standing in a frozen position on the shore. The skunk stood there looking up at him as if to say. "Thank you for saving my life!" Then he turned and walked away, without incident or reward.

"Thanks, Dad!" I said with admiration, and then we both laughed and ran in to tell Mom about the skunk in the flood.

CHAPTER SEVEN

Stumpy's Island

STUMPY'S ISLAND LAY halfway across the river, with the channel separating the cabin from the island. On the other side of the island were sand bars or quiet running water, depending on the river level. The bank on the other side was close to highways 60 and 61. Highway 60 comes all the way up from Prairie du Chien to the west and goes along the river to Gotham. It is a beautiful but treacherously crooked drive. In the fall of the year when the leaves are turning it is breathtaking. Highway 61 comes from the south and joins 60 at the north end of the Boscobel bridge. It separates again about a mile up the river road and goes north to La Crosse. Our cabin was near the south end of the bridge, and just to the east.

Sitting on our porch, we looked directly across the water at Stumpy's Island. One of the best bass and catfish spots was on the south side of the island. Every evening at least one fisherman sat in his boat over there, quietly fishing. Sometimes you would hear a loud yell and look over just as he reeled in a big one. There were always a lot of snags there, so catching a fish was quite a challenge. Fishermen would hate it if they fought a big one and finally landed him, only to find that it was a carp, a buffalo, or a gar. If it was a northern, a big bass, or a catfish, on the other hand, the whooping might continue. The volume of the whoop would kind of give us an idea of the desirability of the fish. It certainly meant a walk to the boat landing for us when a lucky angler came ashore for the night. It was always exciting to see what people caught.

Every year Stumpy's Island moved downstream just a little. Not enough to readily notice, but it always seemed that is was not quite in the same place as it was the year before. As the years went by, it seemed to get a little smaller, too.

During courtship, young people used to boat over to the island with a picnic lunch and a blanket, and some fishing poles for appearance's sake. That's when it was dense with trees and brush. It was fairly private over there, as I recall. It was big enough then to have a cabin on it, which is how it got its name. An old man called Stumpy Anderson use to live there in his cabin. There were a lot of stories about old Stumpy Anderson.

Later, most of the trees fell into the river when the dirt and sand were washed away by the strong current from the main channel. The undercurrents of the lower Wisconsin River are some or the worst in the world. Every year people lose their lives because they misjudge what is just under the surface of that river. The lower end of a sandbar can be a great place for canoe enthusiasts to camp one night, and the next night it could be their death trap. The river washes away the underside of a sandbar and even though it looks all right on top, if you were to stand on it, you could go down and all the sand would suddenly be on top of you. This river is not a place for a novice, or anyone who doesn't know or believe the trickery she is up to at all times.

After several years, Stumpy's Island had moved farther and farther downstream and got smaller and smaller. The early spring was the hardest on the little island. When the winter ice broke up and started moving on the river, huge ice jams would come up against the island and do the most damage.

One year, while I was watching the ice jam go out, I saw the last of the little island go with it. I saw it leave, and it made me sad. Before the day was over, I could see all the way across the river to the other bank. I didn't like the new view. It felt as if nothing would ever be quite the same again with Stumpy's Island gone. Whenever I go to the river and look over in that direction, now, I always think of Stumpy and his island. He died a long time ago, I guess. I'm glad he didn't have to see his island go, as I did.

CHAPTER EIGHT

The Day We Lost the Axe

SPRINGTIME ON THE river brings many welcome changes and some that are not so welcome. As the temperature rises, the runoff from the melting snow and ice causes the river to rise. The ice begins to break up and slowly move downstream. Usually, when there is a gradual warming in the springtime, this process goes almost without notice except to a few avid fishermen who can't wait to get their lines in the water, or to a family whose main sources of entertainment are the changes in the landscape.

Our family fit into both categories, since fresh fish on the table was always a delightful treat, and we liked to watch the river. It seemed as if we had our best luck fishing for sand sturgeon in the early spring, and we couldn't wait until the water warmed up to sixty degrees so that we could start fishing for big catfish. We thought that the yellow gut, or fat gut, of chicken innards was the only bait to use when the water reached that temperature. When the water got any warmer then sixty-five degrees, we would have to use something else to attract the real big catfish, so we were always anxiously waiting for the ice to go out and for the water to warm up.

In most years the breakup of the ice was fascinating to watch because of the small ice jams. Watching the ice pile up higher and higher when it got to the bridge meant that someone in the family would be posted at the window to watch, in order to alert everyone else when it started moving. We all wanted to see it go. The excitement brought oohs and aahs from the children and Dad and Mom alike. Of course, the bigger the ice jam, the more exciting it would be. When the ice moved past the bridge, there was nothing to hold it back. In the open water below the bridge the ice moved quickly on downstream, around the bend, and out of sight. Then all there was left for us to watch were a few big chunks of ice floating down from upstream past the cabin. The ice chunks became smaller and smaller as the movement of the water and the warm spring sun worked their magic.

An exceptionally cold winter meant deep, thick ice. Sometimes it was as thick as twelve to sixteen inches or more. When an early and warm spring follows a hard winter, the breakup can come quickly. And if that happens, fascination can quickly turn to fear, as it did for us one spring during the late 1950s.

It had been a bitterly cold winter and the river had been a solid cake of ice before the spring thaws started. One rainy morning we were sitting at the kitchen table eating a late breakfast, when we heard the loud crashing, crunching sounds outside. Dace yelled, "Ice jam!" and he ran out the door. "Get the kids in the car and get up to the highway, as fast as you can," he yelled.

I grabbed the kids' jackets and rushed them out as far as the porch. "No, wait, don't go. It's too late," he said, "Look at that," as he pointed in the direction of the boat landing. The river water was rushing into the yard and covering the ground all around the cabin. It was coming in fast. We would never be able to get kids out to the car or drive through so much water. The river water behind the jam was flowing in toward us. The ice was barely moving on the river but it wasn't going downstream any longer. Instead it had started coming in our direction. The only barrier between us and the ice were the two big trees that stood about ninety feet apart along the edge of the riverbank in front of the cabin site.

Even though Dace had spent his youth and early manhood on and around the river, he had no idea of the treachery that it could force upon anything that got in its way. We had just never thought that ice was anything we had to be overly concerned about. That morning changed our minds forever.

I had heard of ice jams reaching as much as two stories high in places in northern Wisconsin. I never believed it until now. What we saw before us was a wall of ice eight to ten feet high in places. The mass was easily two hundred feet long and fifty feet wide. It looked like an iceberg. That much force up against a land mass such as the head end of an island exerts so much pressure that it tears up everything in its path. Smaller islands sometimes just disappear or are whittled down to almost nothing. Some trees that have stood for centuries are sawed off or uprooted and began moving downstream along with the ice and water.

This old river has a mind and a spirit of its own. While it permits humans the pleasure of its bounties, it also extracts a price for the abuse

of its freedom. The seven- span bridge that crosses the river near Boscobel is, in a sense, an abuse of that freedom, just as are all the other bridges
and the dams up and down the river.

The bridges that cross the river have spans that are set on columns
made of cement and steel. Trees and debris along with ice slabs get stuck
between the columns and a major ice jam starts to form. Of course, ice
doesn't have to have any obstacle other than more ice in front of it to cause
a jam, but the river bridges are usually the main cause of this happening.

One thing that makes an ice jam so dangerous is the water that builds
up behind it. The free-flowing water begins to rise behind the jam,
increasing the pressure against the ice. As the water rises, slabs of ice
begin to slide on top of each other. The stacked ice causes the water to
rise even higher behind it, in turn causing the ice layers to stack up even
higher and become more and more dangerous and destructive. With the
swift current in the main channel of the river exerting all its force upon
the floating slabs, the ice and the water begin moving in any direction
that is open. Gravitation is toward the path of least resistance. That morning, the path of least resistance was right toward us.

The upheaval of the moving ice crunching and pounding was almost
deafening. At times it sounded like the loud shrieks of an angry woman
as one layer slid screeching across another. The ancient river was on a
different kind of a rampage this time.

Dace yelled for me to bring the mall and to come and help him. He
had the power saw in one hand and an axe in the other and was moving
fast through the rising water toward the ice. I thought he was crazy as
I watched him get upon the layers that had moved in over onto our front
lawn. They were less than thirty feet in front of the cabin. The little ones
were all still out on the porch looking out on top of this monster that
stood menacing in front of them.

Dace threw down the axe, started up the power saw, and begin sawing
away on the top layer. The main part of the huge jam had butted up
against the big trees and at that point was not moving. Dace took advan-
tage of the lull in the movement by working frantically in an attempt to
break it up. It seemed like the futile gesture of a desperate man to me.

I grabbed the heavy mall and moved as quickly as I could through
the cold water, which was now halfway to my knees and rising. He took
the mall from me and hammered it down hard on the ice alongside the
deep groove that he had just cut with the power saw. I crawled upon the

ice with him and watched as he repeatedly made big circular swinging motions with the heavy mall. *Bang!,* down would come the mall and I could hear a cracking sound as the ice split. He stopped and picked up the saw again and began cutting longer and deeper grooves. I chopped at the ice with the axe at first, but was only chipping it, so I took the mall and swung it over my shoulder the way I had just seen him doing. I slammed the mall down upon the ice with all my strength. I wasn't as strong as he was, but the ice was cracking. My arms started aching. If I stopped to rest, he would yell, "Keep going, keep going!"

As the thick, long blade on the power saw sliced downward through the ice I began to realize that his idea was not so crazy after all. I pounded harder and the ice kept making the cracking sounds. Sometimes the split went way beyond the grooves he was making. The most immediate danger was the chance of a block falling away and one of us falling between into a crevice and getting crushed if the ice moved again.

As we worked we began crying out to God for help. Suddenly the main part of the jam started moving again.

Dace screamed at me to get off the ice and I quickly did exactly as he said. Carrying the heavy mall, I began wading away. The water was above my knees, now, so moving quickly through the deep water was difficult. The ice mass was moving right behind me. I knew that I would be crushed if I didn't stay ahead of it. Suddenly the end toward me stopped and began moving in an upstream direction and then turned back out toward the river itself. Dace was still on top of the ice, sawing and at the same time yelling for me to keep moving. The mass underneath him had moved almost forty feet up along the bank and was nearing the boat landing and at the same time had begun moving away from the bank out onto the river. We had managed to split off the whole upper section of ice that ran out to the river, and now that section was making a turn in the water.

Jimmy, our oldest child, was watching from the porch and was screaming for his Dad to get off the ice stack. "Jump, Dad, jump!" he kept yelling. I stood paralyzed with fear, unable to even shout at him. Holding on to the power saw he jumped and landed in the water at the edge of the boat landing. As he waded away from the river, the water was rushing against him and it almost swept him along with it several times. We waded toward each other. We were so cold and were shaking so hard that we could hardly talk. The large severed section of ice

that he had been standing on had moved back toward the middle of the river. The main body of the mass seemed to be slowly moving downstream. We worked our way through the rapidly dropping water and got to the steps that led up to the pump porch.

By now we were both in pretty bad shape. We were wet and cold and exhausted. We went inside and stripped off our wet clothes and wrapped up in quilts that we took from the bed.

Jimmy had seen the whole thing from the porch. He told us in later years that it was the most horrifying memory of his life. At the time, however, he brought a bit of humor to the situation by scolding us for leaving the axe on the ice. What a strange feeling it was to look out and see our axe floating down the river on top of a slab of ice.

Within an hour, most of the water had moved from the banks back into the river channel. Several large chunks of ice were all that remained on the lawn in front of the cabin. The jam had broken loose at the bridge and the water was flowing swiftly, taking with it trees and chunks of ice that had blocked the flow. The crisis was over.

We sat hovered around the stove, drinking hot soup and coffee, just grateful to be alive. There was a great sense of relief and gratitude among us. Whenever we thought about how close we all came to being killed we gave thanks to God for answering our prayers at the very moment that we called to Him for help. We have always believed that He opened the water at the bridge and changed the direction of the ice just for us. There was no other explanation why the jam went out just when it did, and why the ice moved away from our little cabin so quickly.

In the years that followed, when the ice started going out, we would all get in the car and go for a long ride in the country. We didn't stay around to watch. Our fascination with the river opening up in the springtime was gone forever.

CHAPTER NINE

Fishing for the Big Ones

THE MARSHES NEAR Boscobel ran off into a creek that emptied into the river right next to the boat landing. During most of the spring and summer there was a fairly good flow of water in the little creek. When the water level was high in late March and early April, the northern pike would go up the creek into the marshy areas to spawn.

For a three-week period each year, the northerns would leave the river at about 4:45 p.m. and start their swim back into the marsh. You could almost set your clock by them, they were so punctual. Usually you would see a female in the lead with two or three males trailing behind her. It was easy to tell them apart because she was so much bigger. Her belly was full of eggs and she was on her way to spawn. The males would follow close behind to fertilize the eggs as soon as she laid them.

As soon as this evening migration started, I would position myself on the bank with a spear in my hand and one eye watching for any strangers in the area. The game wardens would have frowned on my method of providing fresh fish for the supper table.

I never intentionally speared a female but I did feel that the males were fair game. It didn't seem to me that she needed all those males to do the job, anyway.

There I'd stand on the bank, poised for just the right one to come along, and snap! Just like that I'd have him. Then I'd hurry and put the spear away and clean the fish. After rolling him in flour, I'd deep-fry him. That was the way Dace liked his fish fixed. If it was a trout, he'd want it baked with butter and pepper, but everything else had to be deep-fried.

From creek to plate took less than an hour. The kids were always delighted when they saw that spear fly and me pull out a big old northern. I'd always tell the oldest one, "Don't say anything about this at school or they'll come and put Mama in jail!" When Dace came home from work I got the usual warnings, just before he'd lay into that big plate of deep-fried fish. I'd tell him, "You're the one who taught me how to spear. Why eat a carp when you can have northern pike?"

He had his moments when he watched out for the game wardens, too. At five o'clock every morning he was up and out early. I'd look out and see him quietly moving his boat along his set line that ran from the bank out to the middle of the river. As he worked his way along the finger-size line, he checked the #3 catfish hooks which hung from smaller lines attached to the main line. The hook lines were about a foot long and eighteen inches apart. There were usually about fifty or sixty of these attached to the main line. They were baited every night with small catfish, bullheads, or big suckers. The line stretched halfway across the channel and was anchored on the far end with a hundred-pound sandbag to hold it in place. If his bait was a good size, he might expect to catch a twenty- to forty-pound catfish this way. Don't ever let anyone fool you. You don't catch too many of those big ones with a rod and reel, although it would make a good fish story.

Bankline fishing is another early morning method of fishing. One end of a thirty-foot bankline is tied to a tree. Heavy weights are tied to the end of the line. The best are old window weights. Three or four of these are just enough to anchor the line. Several hooks are placed along the main line, much the same as with a setline. These are baited with minnows or frogs and seem to be attractive to the ten- to fifteen-pound catfish.

The only time Dace was quiet after catching a big fish was when he caught one on a setline or bankline, both of which were illegal. If there was a catch, the big fish were put in a livebox and lowered back into the river and out of sight until they could safely be taken out and supposedly caught on a legitimate line.

It was a joy to watch Dace work his way along the lines in the early morning light. It was a magic time on the river. The wild sounds were all around us. The little ones would be asleep for another hour or two. The smell of coffee would be coming from the pot on the stove and the pancakes were hot from the griddle, waiting for him to come in. There would be a jar of homemade maple syrup that he had made from the soft maple trees that were everywhere in the bottoms.

I'd be standing on the pump porch leaning with my forearms on the rail, waiting and watching, hoping to share in any excitement that there might be. I could see him there about 150 feet from me, as he pulled his way across the river in his wooden flat-bottom boat, quietly taking in his night's catch.

Sometimes when there was a fog on the river, and he'd be out there, silent, hidden from me, I would call out to him in a low voice, "Are you OK?" His answer would come back, just as subdued, "I'm OK.". I would be relieved and overwhelmed by the beauty of the moment. It was a special time for just the two of us, a time that nothing or no one else could ever touch. It was our time.

CHAPTER TEN

Carp Spearing

EARLY SPRING BRINGS a rise in the water level, when the river bottoms and the marshes and swampy areas are under water. This rise washes away a lot of the debris of old cattail reeds and grasses that grew and died during the past season.

This is the time of the year when the carp are good to eat. The water is cold and their flesh is firm. Later, as the weather warms, the flesh becomes soft and muddy. The term muddy means that the dark flesh in the carp increases and the meat becomes softer.

Carp is considered a coarse fish, but they are eaten by many people. Millions of pounds of carp are harvested every year from the Mississippi basin and the Great Lakes and marketed in fish markets in large eastern cities. The carp is one of the most widely-distributed fish in freshwater rivers and lakes.

The carp is a blunt-nosed fish with a small, thick-lipped mouth. It has feelers or barbels that dangle from its upper lip. It has a wide, heavy body covered with large scales.

They say a carp can live to be a hundred years old and weigh up to eighty or ninety pounds. A fish that old and that big would measure up to five feet long. Most of the carp in the Wisconsin are usually one to two feet in length and weigh up to ten pounds.

Carp and buffalo fish are a real disappointment to the average fisherman when he reels in his line and finds one on his hook. When the carp are working in early April, May, and June, many fishermen go spearing. Getting rid of the carp is a goal of everyone who enjoys sport fishing. That's because they interfere with the population of more valuable fish because they eat their eggs and compete for the food supply. They interfere with the duck population as well by uprooting the vegetation of small ponds and backwaters where ducks feed.

Carp can live and breed in muddy and polluted water and can survive extreme changes in temperature. During carp spawning, which usually coincides with the spring rise in the river, they go by the thousands into the backwaters and lay their eggs. The water is alive with them and when you see them flailing around, churning the water, you know it's time to get out your spears or bow and arrows that are used just for the occasion.

A carp spear looks something like a pitchfork except that the spear has thicker, flatter tines that are straight and barbed to hold the fish from slipping off once you have speared it. The average spear has from three to six tines and is mounted on the end of a pole ten to fifteen feet long. Heavy line should be securely attached to the end of the pole so that when you throw the spear beyond your reach, you can retrieve it, carp and all, by pulling on the line. Of course you have to remember to hold on to the line or you will be wading out into the wet murky pond to retrieve your spear.

Dace always made his own spears. He welded a one-inch piece of a spike nail onto the side of the tine near the tip and then sharpened the blunted-off spike to a razor sharpness. He used a brass weld to make a spear strong enough to take a lot of punishment. He mounted his spear on a fifteen- to eighteen-foot shaft of doweling, approximately one and one-half to two inches in diameter. He wanted enough length to his spear so that when he balanced it on his shoulder and walked with it there would be a spring to the handle, meaning that both ends bounced up and down just the right amount to please him. This would distribute the pressure on the pole itself and give him more control when he threw the spear at a big carp that was quite a distance away. If the pole had too much spring in it, it could snap. If it didn't have enough spring, it wouldn't fly as far, he thought. The weight and width of the spear on the end of the pole determined the needed length of the pole. When making his spear, he always started with a longer piece of doweling and kept cutting it off until he had it just the right length.

With all the spears sharpened up and the river level high enough, it was time to check on any signs of the carp working. This meant monitoring for activity all the backwaters visible from the road.

Driving around to the different favorite carp-spearing spots became all-important. He went before work in the morning and again when he came home for lunch and again after he came home in the evening.

He didn't want anyone to get the jump on him when it came to spearing carp. He was so intent on being the first to get a carp in the spring that he cut a big bundle of willow branches and made a fence across the creek next to the cabin. Near the bank where he would be standing, he left an opening about two feet wide in his willow fence for the carp to pass through.

Because the water was still murky, he wasn't able to see the fish very well as they swam from the river up the creek to the backwaters. He solved that problem by putting an old mirror on the bottom of the creek at the opening in his willow fence. The mirror would reflect enough light so that he could see when a fish passed over it. He stood there with his spear in hand, and as soon as a big one cleared the mirror, he speared it.

It was an exciting time of the year when the carp were working. Dace would spear them by the washtubs full. He loved sharing his catch with anyone who would take the fish off his hands.

Family members often took one or two, but that was enough. They weren't too fond of carp. He always gave a tubful to Doc Freymiller who, in turn, gave them to some of his poorer patients, or so he said. Dace always hoped that he kept a few for himself since he was German, and the Germans seemed to know the best secrets of pickling fish. A neighbor, also a German man, named Freddie Bender, loved getting eight or ten of the big ones every year. Freddie would pickle them and they were delicious. He always brought some back for Dace to taste but he wouldn't give him his recipe.

Another friend, Kathryn O'Kane, would take a tubful and cold-pack them. She put a mustard mixture in some of her jars and a tomato mixture in some, but most of her carp was cold-packed with salt and water. She was such a good cook and her cold-packed carp were as good as salmon. Her recipes with the mustard and tomato sauce were the tastiest in the area. No one would want to buy sardines again once they tasted her canned fish.

The best way to prepare carp is to deep-fry them after they have been filleted. That was always a wonderful spring treat. Most of the fish that Dace speared were smoked in his homemade smoker, with hickory or applewood used for the smoking.

He would scale the fish after he cleaned them and cut them in half lengthwise. He then soaked them in a strong brine water. After they soaked for a few hours, he would lay the sections on the shelves of his homemade smoker and light the wood fire.

He made his smoker out of an old gas refrigerator that he no longer had use for. He removed the latch that kept the door closed, so it was safe in case a curious child decided to climb inside it. He put big holes inside the bottom of the refrigerator with a hammer and a big spike nail. He removed the motor and the bottom front cover and fashioned a fire pot where he put wood for burning.

More holes were put near the top of the inside back panel for the smoke to escape after it circulated around the sections of fish that lay on the refrigerator shelves. He built a small chimney on the back side of the smoker and had an opening near the top so that the smoke coming out of the back top of the smoker would go into, and up, the chimney.

The chimney wouldn't have been necessary if he were staying right by the smoker all the time the fish were being smoked, but he needed to do other things around the place and still see when he needed to add more wood to the fire. Had the smoke dispersed in all directions, as it would have without a chimney, he would have been unable to determine from a distance when he needed to add wood to the fire.

Many years after he constructed his smoker, he saw an article in a magazine on how to make a smoker out of an old refrigerator. He always figured that someone saw his smoker and made some money publishing his idea.

If there were still leftover fish, he would put out a sign that said, FREE FISH. TAKE ALL YOU WANT. Then what was left over went into the garden under his corn and tomato plants. The Native Americans would plant a fish in the same hole they put their seeds into, and sometimes so did Dace Chamberlain.

CHAPTER ELEVEN

The Great Escape

Jim Chamberlain III

IN THE AFTERNOON, Mom would make us take a nap and would lie down with us and tell us stories. Sometimes while she was telling a story, she would doze off to sleep but keep right on talking. We waited for this to happen because then the story would take a strange turn of events that usually didn't make much sense. We would all start laughing and she would wake up and straighten the story out.

One day after she was asleep and all the other kids were, too, I heard a truck drive into the yard. I looked out the window and saw Dad dumping something onto our flower garden. I was about six at the time. I wanted to go outside and see him, but getting out was difficult because Mom always latched the hook on the screen door and it was too high for me to reach.

Dad had put two heating vents in the floor, covered by grates. The big one was too heavy for me to lift, but I was able to pull the small one out. The hole in the floor was only about a foot square, just big enough for me to squeeze down through. I slid through the opening and was able to put my feet on the wringer of the washer which was just below the vent. I then eased myself down to the basement floor. I went out the lower front door of the cabin and around back to the garden. I ran to my dad and gave him a big hug. Soon he asked me where Mom and the other kids were and I told him they were asleep and how I got out.

He just laughed and gave me another hug and a kiss and slapped me on my behind and told me to get back inside and to never do that again.

I remember that getting back in wasn't as easy as getting out, but I finally made it and I put the grate back into place. I don't think that Dad ever told on me, but I know that I kept my promise never to go outside that way again.

It was nice to know that I had found a way to get out if I had wanted to. My folks were always guarding us so closely that it felt good to know there was an escape route. One time I just wanted to see if could still move the grate. I wasn't going to break my promise to Dad but I did want to check it out. I tried to pull the grate up out of the floor, and was surprised to find that it had been nailed down. I guess Dad was going to make sure that I didn't break my promise to him.

CHAPTER TWELVE

The Playhouse

CHILDREN NEED A place to play where they can get plenty of sunshine and fresh air, where they have some running room and are safe at the same time. This was one of the most difficult problems the family had to solve because of the river and because of mosquitoes. During warm weather the kids could play on the porch, where they could get the fresh air and some sunshine. They were safe there because we put a latch on the screen door high enough to be out of their reach

The first summer after we moved in, Dace put chicken wire around the bottom of the cabin and put a gate door entrance to the area under the cabin. The kids liked playing there because it was like one big sandbox.

The city of Boscobel sprayed mosquitoes every summer, and the spraying crew would go across the bridge and spray around the Manhattan Club and the cabins below the bridge on that side of the river. They were nice enough to come and spray around our cabin, as well, What a godsend that was! You could actually be outside in the evenings without going crazy trying to fight off hordes of mosquitoes.

It meant that the kids could use their play area under the cabin. It was always dry there, even during a mild rain. The sun shone in on one side in the morning and on the other side in the afternoon.

After the bad winter, we sided over the bottom of the building and made it into a ground-floor room. That meant there was no longer any safe place outside for the children to play, and they didn't like being on the porch, locked in all the time. Of course they had been locked in the play area below, during the previous summer, but they didn't mind that so much. Whenever they had wanted out, they called to me and I came and took them to the outhouse, or upstairs, or just for "walks and talks" as we called those times.

They say that necessity is the mother of invention. It certainly was so in this case. We had to figure out a safe place for them to play, while still allowing me to do my work.

Dace had a big pile of old 2x4s. He cut them into four-foot sections and made a play yard for them. It was twenty feet square. He sanded all the boards so that the children wouldn't get slivers, and painted the whole thing a bright yellow. He put it out near the edge of the property, back from the river, and filled one side with clean sand. It was near a big soft maple that offered cooling shade when they needed it.

At first they loved the play yard, but it wasn't long before they realized that they couldn't climb over the top, and then the complaints started. "This is no fun!" they would say. "We want to come in the house." They didn't, really. They just wanted to run and play wherever they wanted, but it was too dangerous unless one of us was right there to supervise them. They could be seen from the cabin window or the pump porch, and I was constantly doing a head count to make sure they were still there. The main drawback of living on the river was the constant attention that it took to monitor the children. We lived in fear all of the time that one of them would get out somehow and go to the river.

Because they were so unhappy in the play yard, Dace decided to build them a playhouse. He had a pile of boards and some leftover siding and roofing from the cabin. Soon the complaints died down and the building began. The children helped plan it and soon it became a labor of love. Everyone's imagination was at work. The playhouse would have to sit up on poles or something, like the cabin, to keep it from being swept away during high water. Dace decided to build a strong framed base that the little house would sit upon and put the base on skids or runners like a sled. It was eight by ten feet in size and an average adult could stand up inside of it. When it was finished it looked like something out of a fairy tale.

We painted the little house yellow to match the play yard and to use up the old paint we had on hand. It was the only color we had, so that's what we used. We trimmed the house in brown and white and put decals on the front side. It had a door and two windows, which opened and closed. I made curtains for the windows and little braided rugs from old blue jeans. It even had screens on the windows. We nailed these on to keep the older ones from jumping out and escaping the little complex once they got bored with the setup.

A little set of stairs led from the play yard into the playhouse. Now they had a place to make mud pies to their hearts' content. A little blue table and chairs and play dishes make it perfect. Even we parents were invited from time to time to tea parties and mud pie treats.

Whenever the children's young uncles came to visit, they were allowed to sleep in the little playhouse, which made our two oldest children green with jealousy. They thought they should be allowed this great privilege as well. They didn't realize that the young uncles, who were older than our boys, respected and feared the river and were not about to go near it without wearing life jackets.

When high water did come, the little playhouse and the play pen were chained to trees to prevent them from floating away in the water.

The children loved their playhouse. It still stands to this day in the backyard of the family home in Boscobel. It was to become a favorite place to play for the next generation of children, and has even served as a doghouse and a tool shed over the years.

CHAPTER THIRTEEN

Sky Gazing

It was almost fifty years ago when Dace started building his cabin on the river. We spent most of our time there for the next ten years. Back then there weren't many television sets and there weren't any computers in people's homes. Almost everyone's favorite pastime was reading, or listening to the radio, or going to a Saturday night movie.

Dace's favorite radio programs were "Suspense" and the Jack Benny program. He considered Mel Blanc an absolute genius and enjoyed the cartoons that featured his voices and sound effects. He loved Fibber McGee and Molly, and always laughed when Molly would say, "Fibber McGee strong and able, get your elbows off the table!"

Another pastime, enjoyed by only a few nowadays, was sky gazing, as we called it. The night sky was a great source of entertainment, especially during warm weather.

There was a whole lot less pollution in the atmosphere then, and fewer electric lights. Mostly only the cities and towns had lights glaring everywhere. Occasionally a farmer would have a light to illuminate his yard. Other than that, the night and the darkness belonged to each other. Before they were separated the sky was crystal clear and beautiful.

We slept out on the porch when it was warm, giving us a great view of the summer sky. The North Star would hang out over the river bluffs above Easter Rock and would be so bright that you felt you could almost reach out and touch it.

We watched the changing position of the Big and Little Dippers and the Milky Way as the seasons changed and the earth shifted. The moon shining over the river bottoms and reflecting off the water was breathtaking. Moon shadows cast a magic spell over everything they reached. Wild animals sauntered unafraid through the night.

When there was an eclipse of the moon or shooting-star showers, we watched the skies in awe. We came to know all of the planets that were visible to the naked eye.

Moonlight picnics at midnight were a favorite weekend entertainment. We never worried about ants or spiders or other insects bothering us. For those occasions we never lit a lantern. We didn't need more light than the moon gave us.

We still have a midnight, moonlight picnic every now and then. A fishing pole with a hook in the water, the sound of the river, and good food and wine, with the family all laughing and talking. Even a win by the Green Bay Packers can't compare with that combination.

The most beautiful of all sights at night is the Aurora Borealis. Off to the north, lights of all different colors shoot upward into the dark night sky. When we were children our folks told us that these were reflections off the ice in Eskimo land, and if we watched closely we might just see an Eskimo boy or girl walking around. Until they told us that, we thought the world was on fire and the northern lights frightened us. I guess if you saw them for the first time, and didn't know what they were, you might think the world was coming to an end.

To prevent our children from being afraid, we told them the same story, and they searched the night skies for Eskimo boys and girls, too. It wasn't difficult to stir their imaginations into believing that they were truly seeing the children from the far off north.

Another nighttime phenomenon is heat lightning. We used to go up to the top of Shockley Hill on nights when there was heat lightning or northern lights so that we could get a better view of the show. We would just sit and watch for the longest time.

Oh, it took so little to please us in those days. Children today seldom see such sights unless they live in a third-world country where there isn't a neon sign hanging in every window and streetlights turning the night into day everywhere.

There are places where one can still see the night sky with great clarity. The badlands and the desert. I don't know if you can see northern lights or heat lightning in the desert, but the stars certainly are bright, as long as you are someplace away from traffic and shopping malls.

People have come to think of light as being our friend, showing the way through the dreadful darkness. I think it has stolen the darkness from the night and has destroyed our only means of restoring ourselves so that we can cope with the light of day.

Someday, maybe people will rediscover the night and find it as friendly as we did.

CHAPTER FOURTEEN

Feather Island Stew

It was Sunday morning and time to do something that we hadn't done before. Dace said, "Let's all go to Feather Island and spend the day. There is a good, safe sandbar on the upper end and a place where we could wade in the backwaters and pick up clamshells.

"There is even a place where we can swim and the water is both hot and cold," he told the children. The hot summer sun made the water as warm as bath water, but in another place, under a big tree on the south bank, the water comes from a spring and is icy cold. Cold water sounded good to the children on such a warm day. Every one of them wanted to swim in the cold place first.

What we called the backwaters was a long and wide stretch of shallow water. It was about 150 feet wide in places and nearly a mile long. The water was clean and clear, only about a foot deep. Dace had scanned it from end to end and from side to side to make sure that it was safe. It was a perfect place for the little ones to play to their hearts' content.

"We are going to have to make two trips. There is not enough room in the boat for everyone and for the food and supplies, too," Dace said. "I'll take all the supplies for the camp up first and leave them, and then come back and get you."

We filled the cooler with food and milk and put it into the boat along with a big iron kettle, a small pup tent and some blankets (in case the children needed to get out of the sun for a nap), eating utensils, towels, water toys, and other essentials. "It's going to take me a while to take this stuff up the river and set up the campsite, so you have to be patient," he told them.

A friend had let Dace use his outboard motor in return for allowing him to park his boat at the landing. With the sixteen-horse Scott Atwater on the flatbottom wooden boat, the trip up to the island and back would not take long. Dace took off up the river with the supplies and yelled back, "I'll see you in a little while."

The children were so excited to be going for a boat ride on the river. They all put on their life jackets. I made sure that the straps were attached to the back of the life jacket and crossed, then between their legs and attached to the front of the jacket. How they hated those straps, but they understood their purpose after Dace had showed them how their life jackets could slip up over their heads if they didn't keep them fastened.

It wasn't too long before they could hear the sound of the outboard motor. They knew that it was Dad coming back to load all of us in the boat for the trip up the river.

When he pulled into the landing they were so excited that they were jumping up and down and bickering about who would get to sit where, in the boat. Then off we went up the river, with the air blowing our hair back and the wind in our faces as we sped along.

Through a small inlet alongside the sandy beach at the head end of the island, the backwater entered from the main part of the river. It flowed slowly around the south side of the island, past a small island we called Willow Island, then continued westward and reentered the main part of the river at the tip end of Feather Island, about a mile below the inlet.

Everyone got out of the boat and Dace pulled it along through the quiet water. We ran along the edge of the water until we reached the campsite where he had left all the supplies. When we got there, he took the big heavy outboard motor off the boat and set it down on a blanket. Now the boat would float high on the water and would be easy for the children to push around.

This was a child's paradise, a place to run and wade and pick up clamshells. A place to build sand castles, have water fights, or just row the boat around. A place to get plenty of sunshine and just lie in the water and pretend to be swimming.

Dace had a surprise for them on this day. When he had gone into town earlier, to buy food and supplies, he bought a package of big balloons of all different colors. He hadn't shown the children the balloons until now.

"We are going to have balloon races," he announced. Amidst the squeals of delight, he let each child pick a favorite color and they blew up the balloons until they were as big as they could get them. Then he tied a knot in the end of each one and had the children line up across the water. "You're going to put your balloon in the water when I tell you to, and let it ride along without touching it. You can't touch the balloon or you are out of the race. The first balloon to get down where that big tree is, wins the race," he told them, as he pointed downstream about five hundred feet. "Your balloon might come back upstream if a breeze hits it, but don't give up! That will most likely happen to all of the balloons sometime during the race. If your balloon breaks, I'll give you a new one to put in right where your other one broke."

"Now get ready, get set—go! Put your balloons in the water now!" he yelled. The race was on. What a sight, balloons of all colors drifting slowly down the backwater. He was right. A breeze came along and blew them back upstream and the children were calling out to their balloons, "Go down! go down!"

It took a long time for the race to conclude. Balloons and kids were going in all directions. Shrieks of joy and cheers filled the air. Dace stood down across from the tree to announce the winner as soon as one of the balloons crossed the imaginary line between him and the tree. It was hard to believe that one small package of balloons could bring so much happiness to a family as it did that day in the backwaters.

When it was all over, they came back to the campsite for a rest. Everyone was wet and tired after the exciting race. They were laughing and reliving every moment of it. They especially liked the last part

where they waved goodbye to their balloons as they drifted down across the water into the main part of the river. They came back, singing,

"Dark brown is the river,
Golden is the sand.
It flows along forever,
With trees on either end.
Balloons of mine are floating,
Castles made of foam.
My balloon is drifting,
Where will it come home?
Way down the river,
A hundred miles or more,
Other little children
Will bring my balloon ashore."

They ate sandwiches and bananas and cookies and drank milk for lunch. After that, everyone rested on the blankets for a while. Soon it was time to gather wood for a fire to cook the evening meal. There were all kinds of driftwood lying around, so it wasn't long before they had a huge pile of wood and it was time to search for clams. The older ones went back into the water. The little ones slept, and Dace and I read until late afternoon.

When evening approached, we built a fire and drove two forked metal rods into the sand. We put a crossbar through the thick metal handle of the iron kettle and then set it upon the forked rods, suspending the kettle over the fire. We put water and oil and chopped onions into the kettle, then several cans of Campbell's minestrone soup and a can of mushroom stems and pieces. Last we added two pounds of raw hamburger, salt, and pepper. Soon the mixture was simmering and the aroma drifted into the evening air.

The trees were casting long shadows across the water. It would soon be time to go back, but not before eating the wonderful-smelling soup that was awaiting us. Spoons were passed out and soon everyone had a big cup of Feather Island stew, as the children called it. They debated whether it sounded better being called Feather Island soup or Feather Island stew, but in the end they decided on Feather Island stew.

When they were finished eating, they loaded all the supplies in the boat and Dace pulled it back up through the shallow water and took off for the cabin. It would take him a while before he could come back and get us, since he had to unload all of their clamshells as well as the supplies.

They took one last dip in the water and we slowly walked along the sandbar back up to the inlet where we waited for their dad to return. "Mom, do you think we could come back next Sunday?" they asked. "We'll see," I said.

Many times in the years that followed, we went back to this quiet place and enjoyed its solitude. When the children grew to adulthood, Feather Island stew would remain one of their favorite meals during their annual family deer hunting gatherings. It always brought back good memories of a balloon race and clamshell gathering and that wonderful day we spent at our own special place in the wilderness.

CHAPTER FIFTEEN

The Treasure Hunt

ONE OF DACE'S favorite pastimes was reading. He was one of those people who read everything he could get his hands on, even labels on cans of food, or directions on flyers that came with something we bought. He especially loved stories of hidden pirate treasures. If he ever had a fantasy, it probably involved finding an old map and tracking down a pirate's booty.

He bought old books at every opportunity. He went to estate sales, scrounged every secondhand store, and even went through dumpsters at the State Historical Society to pick up discarded books. Not only did he read the books, but he would check to see whether someone left something in them. Once he found an old will that was dated in the thirties, and he attempted to look up the named relatives to give it to them.

It was probably because of the excitement that this kind of thing held for him that he came upon the idea of "The Treasure Hunt," which became one of the most important experiences in the lives of his children and grandchildren. Almost everyone in the family was involved in at least one of these expeditions. The hunt would usually be focused around one of the children who was at the age of still believing in Santa Claus and who would not question certain aspects of the discovery, such as the date on a coin found in the treasure.

A treasure hunt might occur after a big disappointment of some kind, or as a way of celebrating a special day in the child's life. Whatever the reason, it would take many weeks in planning before the actual hunt took place. It would involve finding just the right old boards to make the chest, which would be about a foot long, eight inches wide, and ten inches high. Then Dace would make a round-topped lid and two old-looking, ornate hinges and a latch. The box would be lined with red or blue velvet-like material. Brassy metal strips were nailed in two or three places across the rounded lid and then around the box itself.

When the box was closed, it looked like a miniature trunk. Sometimes Dace would shellac the wooden parts of the box and shine the brass strips. When it was finished, it would be a beautiful little chest—one that would most likely sit on the child's desk for years to come.

After he had made the chest, he had to figure out what he would put into it that would excite and amaze that particular child.

Dace thought that every chest must have some gold coins. Since gold coins weren't exactly in abundant supply, he would have to make them. He would do this by first making a plaster of paris mold. He would then take a round metal slug approximately the size of a fifty-cent piece or a silver dollar and press the slug half way down into the wet plaster. When this was dry he would scrape the plaster around the slug until the area was smooth. Then he would make small trenches in the ends of the mold so that there would be an opening on one end for the hot liquid lead to be poured in and on the other end for the excess to drain out.

He would then line the flat area with wax paper and make the top half of the mold much the same way. When the mold was dry, he would run his jackknife blade along where the wax paper divided the mold, and ease it apart. The slug and the wax paper were then removed. He'd make several of the molds so that the coin making would not take so long. If he had slugs of different sizes, he would line them up in the same mold with enough space between them so that they didn't touch. He'd make a trench between the holes and oil the mold where it was to come together. When he was finished, it was time to make the coins. He was no stranger to working with hot lead and homemade molds. That is how he made all of his own sinkers for fishing.

After he mounted his molds in a vice to hold them tightly together, he put pieces of lead into his small lead pot and melted them down with a blow torch. Then, ever so gently, he poured the hot lead into the tiny trench at the top of each mold.

Once it had cooled, he would gently pry open each mold by running the thin, sharp blade of his jackknife along the oiled crack. He would ease out the warm coins, making certain that he didn't damage the mold. Over and over he repeated this process until he had enough coins for the purpose.

The lead coins were heavy, like gold, but they were dark gray in color. After he filed the edges smooth, he would get a small bottle of gold paint and paint each one of them, sometimes giving them two or three coats until, to a child's eye, they looked authentic. He would put the painted coins in the sun to dry, out of the sight of the children.

It always amazed me to see the lengths he would go to when it came to pleasing the little ones. It seemed that he took as much pleasure in planning the details as in the event itself.

Dace thought that a treasure chest should have jewelry in it, so it became my job to find some. What worked best was to share the anticipated treasure hunt plans with the older women in the surrounding nursing homes and ask that they go through their old jewelry and sell or donate their old baubles that they no longer wanted. Even broken necklaces were fine. After removing the strings, Dace would put the loose beads in the chest.

Sometimes a small gold picture frame or figurine was included, and foreign coins were added to the booty if we could find any. Anything that made the contents of the chest look colorful, exciting, and genuine was added, until it was nearly full of trinkets of various kinds.

Now it was time for mapmaking. The treasure map had to look authentic, so Dace would take a piece of an old brown paper bag and stain it with oil and wipe it dry. Then he would tear it to make sure that it had no particular shape and he would burn it along the edges. He would then wrinkle it and smooth it out again so that it looked old.

At last, it would be the time to bury the treasure chest. Dace would take the chest and the map and go upriver to the island depicted on the map. He would find a big tree and walk off so many paces and mark it on the map. Then he would change directions and walk so many more paces and mark that also. Two or three direction changes later, the treasure chest was buried and an X was put on the map to mark the burial place. In one corner of the map he would make big letters. N, S, E, and W, to indicate the points of the compass, and finally it would look just like an old storybook treasure map.

When he had buried the chest, he would smooth out the sand so that the area looked undisturbed. When he returned from his little trip he would come in the house and slip the map into an old book and give me a wink which meant everything was ready. The time for the discovery of the map was at hand.

After a while he would call to the unsuspecting child and say, "Hey, let's look at this old book that I just found. Maybe there's a good story in it that I can read to you." Weeks of preparation had gone into this moment. The scene wasn't always exactly the same, but it would often go something like this.

Together they would open the book and start looking through it for the story. When they discovered the map, he would act excited. "What's this?" Dace would say, and all the while he would be watching the child's face. "What in the world have we found in this old book? What have we got here?" he'd go on, as he opened the map. "I think this looks like an old treasure map. What do you think?" By that time the child would be so excited he would agree with anything Dace said.

I would come over and ask what was going on. Dace wouldn't say a thing. He would be pretending to study the map. Finally the little one would answer, "Mom, me and Dad found a treasure map." Then I would look at the great discovery and just keep saying to the child, "Oh, my gosh, a real treasure map. Oh, my gosh. Where did you find this?"

"We found it in this old book!" I would finish off with a few more enthusiastic comments and ask him some leading question, such as, "Where do you think this place is? Is it around here someplace? Can you tell?"

That would prompt a closer examination of the map. They would go to the table, then, where the map could be laid out flat so that it could be studied better. Dad and the lucky child would be the only ones doing the map checking. The rest of us just had to be content to look on. After all, they were the ones who found it.

A big part of the child's joy was in figuring out just where the treasure was. The first time Dace created a treasure hunt was for our oldest son's sixth birthday. Jimmy had wanted a party but he knew no parents would let their kids come. Not to the river! He was so disappointed.

When they examined the map, they discovered the image of a big feather-shaped island. Jimmy knew all about Feather Island and he immediately guessed where the treasure was buried.

With that figured out, it was time to go and start looking around on the island. The two got shovels and a canteen of water. Digging for buried treasure is thirsty work.

Before they started out, the big direction indicators on the map were matched to the ones on the compass. Then, after a brief lesson on how to use a compass, the compass and map were safely tucked into their pockets. After that, it was time to load their supplies into the boat and put on their life jackets. Then off they went up the river after buried treasure.

It was their map. They were the ones who found it in the old book, so it was their adventure. The rest of the family would just have to wait until later to be told about the details of the treasure hunt.

Jimmy thought that it was so great that all of this was happening on his birthday. Now he didn't care that there was no old party. He was too busy to bother with other kids or a party. He had something better to do. He was off on an adventure with his dad—an adventure that would be with him for the rest of his life.

Chapter Sixteen

The River

Robin Chamberlain Transo

Our life was down there on the river. Sitting on its banks watching the current, my parents would build stories around her as if she were alive. Those stories would be mixed with both truth and fiction as in the story where my mother would tell us that the devil lived under the river. "He is waiting for you to get close enough so he can reach up and pull you under," she would say.

As proof, she would point to a branch bobbing up and down in the river. "See," she would go on to say, "There is his hand just waiting to grab you."

Mom, smoking her cherry-blend tobacco and puffing on her long-stemmed briar pipe, would tell us stories for hours. Sometimes, we would lie on our backs and look deep into the sky and the clouds. Eagles and hawks floated on the wind above the river cliffs. They stared into the water as intently as we stared at them.

Dad would skin catfish and talk about his dreams. What the garden would produce, what kind of fish he was going to smoke in the smoker, or how he would build a special boat.

I would sit and watch my parents build and struggle through lean times to make things good for us. In my mind, things were always good, especially on the river.

When we were little, we would take our baths in the big minnow boxes in the backwaters of the river. Swimming in the early morning mist with the minnows that my mother had seined the evening before.

"Don't step out too far," she would warn. When she dipped her net, minnows would rush away and tickle our cold legs. It was like being in a different world. I still remember so well those early morning baths. The mist held the smell of the river and the sun would sneak in over the water to lift itself up to its cloudy perch on the cliffs.

In times like these, colors became surreal, with blue-grays and a grainy mix of greens falling across the hills. Pink lights streaked across deep bluish-green water, while thousands upon thousands of reflective lights bobbed upon its surface under the early morning sun.

As we left the water, into warm bath towels, Mom would carry up the minnows and pour them into an old Coke cooler that stood near the pump porch. Soon the fishermen would be putting in their boats and would want to buy fresh bait.

Those were the happy times, but life on the river is not always steadfast or predictable. As I think back on it now, our lives as young children were a daily fantasy woven into nature and all of its secrets. Our walks became entangled with mystery and truth that opened the river and its backwaters like Christmas boxes filled with riches. Wealth in monetary terms was not something we understood as children, but the gifts given to us by the Wisconsin River placed us in another world, a world that was attainable but not often sought out by others who lived in town.

Our parents were afraid of what the river could do to us, yet they gave it to us as we grew rather than see us go up the road and hang out in town. "Go to the forest and play!" they would say, but always were the warnings about wandering too far or going where we weren't allowed.

With a smile on my face, I would wink at my younger brothers and sisters and rally them around for a journey into the yet unknown. We would grab our walking sticks and hike bare-legged and barefoot into the swamp like so many castaways on a deserted island. "Today," I would announce, "we are all going to the chapel to plan our journey." Into the aged willow trees we would turn as our trek led us down a path known only to ourselves.

Soon we would come to the Castle Tree with its huge broken branch that we called "The Bridge." The old willow was so big that all of us could climb up the bridge at one time and stand on it to look over the path below.

We played as if we were the lost boys of Peter Pan, all dirty and wet from crossing the swamp, but this tree was used to us as we were. It offered itself to us and was healthy as long as we came to visit it. Sometimes we would cradle in its branches a beloved pet that died an untimely death. "You care for our pet," we would say with tears in our eyes. Our loss was somehow consoled by the strength of this forest grandfather.

After leaving the great willows, we would make our way to that part of the forest we called "The Chapel." It was actually a clearing in a grove of poplar trees. It got its name because if you looked up to the sky in that area, you could see a huge letter J opening to the sky. "J stands for Jesus," I remember saying to the younger ones. We felt that in every way this was a sacred place. The smell of the earth and swamp surrounded us. The rustle of the poplar leaves in the wind always lifted our spirits. The beauty of the colors and earth tones danced in the reflected light before our eyes and all seemed more majestic as we looked up and were reminded of Jesus.

After first discovering this place, we ran home and told our parents to come and see what we had found in the forest. One or the other would always come with us whenever we asked, if only to support our finds with their presence. Somehow, that is all we needed at times, the love of the river bottoms and being with our parents in that place.

As the little ones got older our trips took us across streams and into forests filled with buttercups and wild grapevines spreading across trees that my grandfather might have enjoyed as a boy. Our walks took us down dog trails and into fields of wild grasses, sometimes much farther away from home then we should have been. Once we found an area where the sand was so soft that it acted just like quicksand. When we threw our sticks into the soft sand they soon disappeared and we knew that we would, too, if we weren't careful. We decided to stay away from this place and keep quiet about it until we were older. We knew then that Mom wasn't exaggerating when she told us that there were places in the swamps that could swallow you up, as fast as the river would, if we got too close.

Almost always in the late fall, our walks would end up in a special marsh area that was filled with cattails. Once we were there during the season when the cattails start splitting and the seeds fly away in the breeze. That day, the greatest cattail battle of all times took place. We began hitting each other with the heads of the cattails and the brown heads burst and the cotton like seeds filled the air. It was like no feather pillow fight you could ever imagine.

The wind blew the seeds up into the air in a great ticker tape flurry. When we stopped, we watched the wind carry off the vestiges of our great battle. What a sight! We sure had a great time that day, and we went home exhausted. We were the "River Kids." Our lives were filled with love for each other, and we felt united by the river that flowed through our veins.

Now so much of the dog trail has changed, because the river creates endless change. The great willows are gone now and young trees are carving out new chapels, as yet undiscovered. We were blessed with a childhood of fantasy and dreams that we will forever hold in our hearts and our spirits. The Wisconsin River and its backwaters and swamps and the bottomland will be part of us forever.

CHAPTER SEVENTEEN

The Deadly October Rise

IT HAPPENS ONLY once every hundred years, the old timers tell us—an unnatural high rise in the water level. October of 1959 was one of those years. The river went wild. Everything in her path changed, including our lives.

Small islands were swept away and new ones were formed. Big islands were made either bigger or smaller, but were certainly not the same as they were before. Huge trees went crashing down the river. Sandbars appeared where there had been deep flowing water, as the channel carved a new course down between the Wisconsin River bluffs.

People who lived in the towns along the lower Wisconsin were aware that the water had risen higher than they had ever remembered, but they were unaware of the force behind the angry river or just how quickly it had happened.

Dace went to work in town in the early morning. The water was over the first landing, but we thought that it had just about reached its peak.

We could look down through the vents in the floor and see that some things in the basement were now covered with water. It was over the top of the old Maytag washing machine and the Round Oak stove was almost submerged. We had brought everything up onto the porch that would be damaged by water, so we felt prepared to weather the rise as we had done so many times before.

Because the water was up, Dace had to take the boat out to the main road, to get to the car. This meant that the children and I would be in the cabin for the day with no way to leave.

We had gone through these kinds of trials so many times before that we were used to it, and this rise in the river was of no great concern to us. It just meant another exciting experience. We were surrounded with water and we would have a chance to see some wildlife that we weren't used to seeing.

During high water, small screech owls would come and perch on our pump porch. Once in a while the big old barn owls would do the same. Sometimes an otter, a mink, a fox, or some other wild animal would take refuge and wait out the rise with us. The animals that came didn't appear to be afraid of us, so it was fun to sit on the porch and talk to them. I always made certain that the children didn't leave the main porch, not only because of the high water, but you never know if a wild animal might get frightened and bite. Wild animals often carry rabies as well.

About mid-morning, I looked down through the vent with a flash-light and was shocked to see that the water had come up so much higher. I became genuinely concerned. After that, I watched the bottom of the bridge, which was a block or so downriver from the cabin. It seemed as if every time I looked, the water was closer to the road bed of the bridge.

Around eleven o'clock in the morning, the water was within two feet of the floor of the cabin. I had never heard of water coming up so fast. I became very frightened, then, because I didn't expect Dace home until after work in the late afternoon.

There was nothing that I could do, since we didn't have a second boat. I didn't want to frighten the older children, so I began praying silently to myself. We had six children by this time. The youngest was only two and a half months old. The oldest was seven. It was a Satur-day, so they were all at home.

I knew that if the rise continued at this pace we would be in serious trouble within a couple of hours. When I looked out the window to the east, I could no longer see the top of the small barn or the tops of my clothesline poles.

By now the water was so swift that I feared we might be swept away. I wondered whether we could be saved, even if someone did come for us by boat. Further, our boat had no motor at that time. I started making an SOS sign on a sheet. I planned on hanging it out the west window so that anyone going across the bridge might see it if they happened to look upriver.

Suddenly, I heard shouting. I ran out onto the pump porch and saw Dace coming in the boat. He was coming in fast from the roadway. The swift water swept him along. He rowed the boat toward me up to the porch and I grabbed the anchor out of the front of the boat. He stepped out onto the porch.

By that time I was almost crying with relief. Then he told me that we might have a rough time making it back out to the road, rowing against the current.

We planned out what we had to do. He would first take the two older children and put them in the car. He would instruct them that if we didn't come back that they should walk into town to Grandma's house and tell her that we didn't come back to the car. They were to tell her to get help for us.

We put life jackets on Jimmy and Robin and they left the pump porch, waving at me, not realizing the danger we were in. The oldest ones were taken out first so that they could care for the younger ones as he brought them out. I could see the struggle Dace was having, trying to row against the current. I wondered whether it was possible for him to get back to the road. I said all the prayers that I knew. I asked St. Christopher for protection.

About twenty minutes later, I could hear Dace's shouts again. It was hard to hear him over the roar of the rushing waters. Then I saw him, coming the way he had come before. Again, I grabbed the anchor when he reached the top step of the pump porch.

We quickly put the life jackets on Rock and Peter and positioned them in the boat with repeated warnings against moving around. They, like Jimmy and Robin, were not allowed to sit in the seats, but were made to sit down in on the bottom of the flat wooden hull. Then Dace started rowing away from the pump porch with his second load of precious cargo. He said to me, "I will be back soon. Now you believe that!" I knew he was scared and I knew that he had to be getting very tired rowing against such a strong current.

My prayers increased in intensity. "Please, God. Just let him get there with these two." The rowing was harder this time. He wasn't sure whether the water was faster, or whether he was losing his strength.

When he did finally get to the car, he instructed the two older children to watch the two younger ones and not let go of their hands if they had to walk to Grandma's house. There was deep water on both sides of the road, and heavy traffic on the highway, with people looking at the high water.

I couldn't tell how much time had passed, but it was taking longer than the first trip. I had taken the fuses out of the fuse box earlier, when it looked as if the water was going to come up to the electrical wiring high on the basement wall, so that we wouldn't be electrocuted. We didn't have a windup clock, so I had no way of telling the time.

More time passed and still he hadn't come back. I began to think that he must not have made it to the road or maybe he just couldn't get back for us. I kept telling myself what he had told me as he was leaving. He would come back for me, and I was supposed to keep believing that. That remark scared me, but it was all I had to go on.

I had a cloth bag packed with a change of clothes for the children and all the diapers that I had. I sat on the porch holding the two little ones close to me and prayed that God would spare them, too. Mike was only about eighteen months old and Mark was less than three months old. I kept thinking that they were too young to die. I felt real lonely sitting there with the water swirling all around us. As we waited, I tried to listen for Dace's voice calling but couldn't hear anything. We were there on the porch for what seemed to be a very long time. I kept thinking, "Have faith, just have faith."

Off in the distance I thought I heard a faint voice. I put the children on the cot and went out onto the pump porch. Then I saw him, coming around between the trees. He was coming so fast. He guided the boat toward the pump porch. I could see he was having a lot of trouble, now, controlling the boat's direction in the powerful current.

As soon as the boat bumped the porch, I grabbed the anchor. Dace got out, looking frightened and exhausted. "We have to hurry," he said. We put the life jacket on Mike. Dace put the other one on me with the baby strapped to my chest, in a sort of reverse papoose fashion. I felt safe for the first time in hours. I knew that if the boat tipped we would at least have a chance to float in the river and would probably wind up on the other side somewhere, maybe even miles away. I knew that the water always takes you to the land, eventually. I remember thinking that at least we had a chance of living through this.

I asked Dace why it took so long this time and he said that it was a lot harder getting out than the first time. He told me how he had instructed the kids. We loaded the bag of clothing into the boat. I could tell he was really tired. I tried to get him to stop and rest for a while before starting out again, but he refused to wait any longer.

As soon as we were positioned in the boat, he started pulling hard on the oars. I could tell that it was taking every bit of strength he had to keep the boat from being swept away down the river.

Dace made a wide circle and rowed over the tops of the clothesline poles and out over the top of the little barn that was not much more than boards nailed to four trees with a roof over it. It was at least six feet high and had been used for an old cow that we had had several years before. I couldn't believe that I was looking down on top of the roof and that it was a good foot and a half under water. Dace made his way out toward the swamps and I wondered why he was going out in that direction. He told me that he was putting the trees between us and the river itself to be on the safe side. He later told me that his arms were so tired that he was afraid he would have to anchor us to a tree so that he could rest. We worked our way along the back swamps over the rushing water and finally made it to the road. I could hardly believe that the water was up to the highway road bed. We could see the children sitting in the car. They were cheering us on. Finally we came to the road beside the car and I threw out the anchor. At last, it was over. Dace was almost ready to collapse.

When we were all in the car, Dace bowed his head and led us in a prayer, thanking God. We were out and we were all alive. Right then it seemed that that was the only thing in the world that mattered. When he started praying, I realized how frightened he must have been. He had risked his own life three times to save us, struggling against the powerful current to bring us to safety.

I asked him later what had made him come home in the middle of the day when we thought earlier that everything would be all right. He said that late in the morning he started having a nagging feeling that he should come and check on us. He said that he got to wondering what I would do if one of us got sick or hurt.

That was the last day we ever lived on the Wisconsin River. About two hours after we got out, the cabin tipped. Had we been in it, we all would have drowned. Some time later the cabin broke loose and floated down the river. The current had been so strong that it had washed out the footings under the poles that held the cabin up. It had washed away the cement floor and the basement walls.

Dace had started building the cabin in 1950 and now here it was nine years later and it was gone, swept away with the high water. He was only thirty years old and I was twenty-six when we left the cabin for the last time. Those were hard years but they were the happiest of our young lives.

Dace's father had bought a small four-room house in town, on the edge of the swamps. He sold the house and two lots to us, for one hundred dollars. What a wonderful gift! It was heaven, having so much more room, but it was still crowded with six children. Later, as the family grew, we bought an old country schoolhouse and connected it to the four-room house. Dace restructured the whole place and turned it into a nine-bedroom home. That has been the family home ever since.

CHAPTER EIGHTEEN

The Fruits of the Land

DACE LOVED TILLING the soil and planting things. During his lifetime he planted thousands of trees of one kind or another—pine, walnut, soft maple, apple, cherry, plum, and even a peach tree or two. He planted shrubs, flowers, and almost every kind of vegetable that grows in Wisconsin including asparagus, horseradish, and rhubarb.

He gathered every kind of a berry that grows wild in this area, and a few things that the average person wouldn't think of. He even gathered chokecherries that I made into jelly and served with the duck and turkey every Thanksgiving and Christmas.

Usually we put up around seven or eight hundred quarts when the garden was productive. The record year was when we put in an acre-size garden. That year, we put up 1,400 quarts of vegetables, fruits, jams, and jellies.

Dace bought a couple of new plastic thirty-gallon garbage cans which he filled with shredded cabbage and salt and water to become sauerkraut.

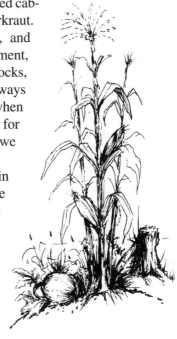

For many years, dandelion, grape, and chokecherry wine worked in the basement, and beer was brewed in thirty-gallon crocks, bottled, and stored on shelves. It was always a nice treat when company came—but when the company started coming around just for the treat and outstaying their welcome, we stopped making it.

Later, we owned eighty acres of land in Crow Hollow. We built a small barn there and kept some beef cattle and pigs, which we fattened for slaughter for the winter's meat supply.

Most of the tree planting was done on the Crow Hollow land. Everyone in the family took part, just as they did in caring for the huge garden and the gathering and preserving of what we grew there. Our land was eleven miles from the family home, so when there were pigs to be fed it meant a daily trip to Crow Hollow with fresh whey from the creamery in town.

In the spring of the year there were morel mushrooms to gather and dehydrate for winter use. We gathered and dried wild onions from the river bottoms, as well. Both of these delicacies were used in the wild rice stuffing for my recipe for black duck. We always had black duck along with the turkey at Thanksgiving and Christmas.

Black duck was one of my own special recipes. I made plum butter from our own plums or from wild plums, cooking the butter down to where it became almost black and thick as tar. We called it plum tar. I added cinnamon sticks and some other spices, which also added to its dark color. After I stuffed the duck with wild rice dressing, I smeared it with the plum tar and roasted it. It was served with my chokecherry jelly. Gourmet cooks would love to have some of those recipes. That clear pink jelly alongside the black duck was a sight to see.

Another one of my recipes that always graced the holiday table was banana squash pie. It got its name from the banana squash that I used to make it from. It was far better than pumpkin pie, but twice as much work to make. The Christmas cake was made from scratch with flour made from cattail roots.

Dace was a good cook, too. Whenever he could get a live beaver, we would have stuffed beaver. The animal could weigh up to seventy pounds and the meat was as tasty as beef. He always prepared beaver by stuffing it with sage dressing and wrapping strips of bacon across it, roasting it whole.

He fixed raccoon a couple of times, but nobody was too interested in eating anything that looked like a dog when it was in the roaster, so he had to eat that himself. Rabbit, squirrel, wild duck, pheasant, and venison were not uncommon on our table when they were in season. Dace was usually the one who prepared the meals that included wildlife.

Dace could do other things that were not generally thought of, at that time, as a husband's chores. He would sit down at the old New Home treadle sewing machine and make his own gun cases and trapping bags or anything else that he might need to carry things in or cover something with.

There was never any extra money around, and as a result the family was considered by friends, relatives, and the community to be quite poor.

The children were sometimes scorned by their schoolmates because they didn't have as many new things to wear or show off as the others. When they came home from school feeling bad about this, we told them that they were the richest kids in town because they were loved so much. We said that money doesn't make a person rich, regardless of how much of it one has. I doubt that they ever believed this until after they had become adults and realized that they had been well prepared for life, and taught to survive under the most difficult of circumstances. Then they remembered that they often had a wonderful and exciting time in growing up.

Chapter Nineteen

Maple Syrup Making

ALONG ABOUT THE middle of February, Dace would start collecting gallon cans. He had everyone he could think of saving them for him. Restaurants, the school cooks, and even the cooks at the hospital would put their empty gallon cans aside and he'd pick them up and bring them home until he had a couple hundred of them. Then he would punch two holes at the top of each can and add a wire handle.

Next he would make spigots to tap into the trees so that the sap would flow out. He would cut sumac branches that were about a half-inch across and cut them up into twelve-inch lengths. Then he would take a red-hot length of a wire coat hanger and burn the pithy center out of the sumac. When it was hollow all the way through and he had the center hole big enough to allow the sap to flow through, he would cut it into four-inch lengths and whittle one end down so that it would go into the hole in the tree more easily. He would need one, two, or three spigots for each tree, depending on the size of the tree and how much sap it would yield.

He would need a vessel to cook down the sap once he had collected it, and a pit of some kind to place it in for the boiling process.

For the vessel, he took a 250-gallon oil drum and laid it on its side and cut off the top one-third of the drum with a cutting torch. The ends of the metal drum were left intact, except for a hole that he put near the top of one end, so there would be a place for taking hold of the drum and lifting it around. The drum was big enough to hold a hundred gallons of sap at a time and worked just as well as the old-fashioned kettles that they used in sugar camps years ago.

Most maple syrup manufacturers today use modern techniques and tools, but they lose the romance that the old-time sugar camp held for syrup-makers and tasters. There is no doubt which syrup is better, in my book.

Along the bank in the backyard was an old, loose, rock wall that was about three feet high. Dace dug a long pit in the yard with the front side of the pit coming out at the rock wall. Some loose rocks were removed so that the opening to the pit was large enough to get wood in under the cooking drum. He lined the pit with bricks and made it just wide enough at the top to allow the drum to lie on its side on top of the brick pit without falling into the fire beneath it. He made certain that the elongated pit was deep enough so that it would hold a good bed of hot coals. He could shove several five-foot pieces of wood into the pit at a time. Tree limbs and branches were used to fuel the fire pot. If he used a larger log for the fire, one that was maybe ten or fifteen feet long, he would simply feed it into the pit until the first part of it burned down, then push it in further until it was completely burned. He called that the hillbilly way of keeping the fire going, since it didn't require sawing a thick log into five-foot lengths.

He tested out his setup by boiling soapy water in the drum, and then clear water, until he could no longer see any traces of oil in the water. The drum had to be immaculately clean or the syrup would be tainted. Making certain that there wasn't any oil residue left required that he repeat the cleaning and water boiling procedure over and over. The final test was to make a cup of instant coffee from the boiling water. If the coffee tasted good, and there was no taste or smell of oil, he knew the drum was clean.

When he was ready to make syrup, he waited for the right weather before starting to tap the trees. It had to be cold enough at night to freeze and warm enough in the daytime to thaw. That is when the sap starts flowing. This usually happens in March but can start in late February, or even extend on into early April.

By watching the icicles on the eaves, Dace knew when it would be time to get his brace and bit and supplies and head for the river bottoms. He would drill a hole into the tree past the sap line and pound a spigot in at a slight angle so the sap would run down the hole in the spigot. Then he would drive a big nail in the tree above the spigot and hang a pail on it. If conditions were right, it wouldn't be long before you could hear the *poing, poing, poing* of the sap hitting the bottoms of the empty gallon pails. He would go from tree to tree until he had all his pails hung. The sap brought strange music to the woods with its variety of dripping notes.

Soft maple trees are abundant in the river bottoms. The trees closest to the fire pit were chosen because carrying sap to the cooking drum was a tedious job. In the old days they had horses and bobsleds with collecting barrels to gather the sap. Dace didn't have that luxury, so it meant carrying the sap to the fire in five-gallon buckets. It also meant many, many trips, since the sap had to be gathered at least twice a day at the peak of the season. Nothing was so upsetting as to go to a bucket and find it overflowing with sap.

In some years the water would be up in the bottoms and we would go from tree to tree in a boat to gather the sap. While this was inconvenient for us, the children loved checking the buckets with the boat.

Hard maple trees are better than the soft maple for syrup-making because it takes a lot less sap to make a gallon of syrup. Twenty gallons of hard maple sap or thirty gallons of soft maple sap should yield about a gallon of the thick brown syrup, in our experience. It may be that the hard maple trees grow where there is less water and therefore produce a sweeter sap. Soft maples that grow in wet areas most likely have a more diluted sugar content.

After we gathered the sap, we strained it and poured it into the big drum. A good fire was stoked up to keep the sap boiling. The fire must be maintained twenty-four hours a day. It takes a long time to boil down a hundred gallons of sap, and of course as time goes by more sap is added to the cooking pan.

The time passes with story telling, visits from friends and neighbors, and sometimes music and singing. Wieners and marshmallows are roasted and even some beer drinking goes on during the late hours of the night. It is a happy time and many of the people who stop by sometimes stay all night long to enjoy the glow of the fire and the festivities.

As the sap boils down, it becomes dark and thick. When it reaches a certain stage we transfer it to a large kettle, such as a sixteen-quart canner, and finish it off on the kitchen stove. It is strained again and after it is brought to a boil on the stove, egg whites are added to collect any residue. Then it is strained for the last time and cooked to the preferred thickness. At this point the syrup should be a clear brown color and is ready for use. While the syrup was still piping hot, we poured it into sterilized fruit jars and sealed them. Enough was saved for cornbread, waffles, or pancakes, which would be the very next meal if the diligent crew had anything to say about it.

Fragments of a Dream

Robin Chamberlain Transo

My life is pressed along rivers
like molded maple sugar candy...
as repeated dreams carry freedom
on the wings of indigo night birds...

Its love is my healing, a soul tonic,
smooth after taking and fluid in the giving...
Leaving whispers in the trees
caressed and haunted by secrets from childhood.

My fingers slide along currents
ever changing in its need to correct the landscape...
I lead others to the river, a safe place to think,
We pull purple dragons out and plant sunflowers in their dung.

Time betrays me,
as my grip slips on the wet vines that cling to me...
forgetting the promises of blush and tickle bouquets
I relive tender longings and centered memories.

I cross endangered bridges and unexplored paths
that pretend to be avenues through a forest of thought...
and find my mind silhouetting a spring breeze
in hues of blue greens and pinks, to paint a mist of
remembrances.

River mud, squishing between toes that
are testing deeper and ever forgiving challenges...
River willows hauntingly whip at me in the wind
and are cut down for dream catchers.

Dream catchers that catch all that is bad and waits
for dissipation like so many visits to the confessional.
Dreams come again on the wings of birds,
flying high above soft maples where the sugar begins.

CHAPTER TWENTY

Little Bear

Robin Chamberlain Transo

WHEN I WAS still quite young, we took our puppy Little Bear with us to check the trap lines. She had a way of getting herself into trouble, but we promised Dad that we would keep an eye on her and took turns tucking her in our coats because of the cold. It was early spring, the snow was still on the ground, but the ice on the river was thawing and walking out to some of the trap lines was a bit tricky. Thin ice was every-where under the snow, but there really wasn't any way to tell without tapping the bottom of a large walking stick on the ice as you walked, to hear the difference from one place to another.

After we walked in the river bottoms for about half an hour or so, we came to a bend in backwaters off the main channel of the river. The sun was shining so bright it was almost blinding off the snow. We could hear water under the ice and Dad warned us about staying back as he approached the dangerous ice. Just as he did so, one of the younger chil-dren put the puppy down, but the puppy didn't stand still and ran out behind Dad on the ice. All of a sudden she stepped through a very weak spot on the ice and fell in. She disappeared almost as she fell and a great wailing went up from all of us. We were sure she was gone. The river current was strong and she was so little. How could she fight such a thing?

My dad quickly recognized the situation for what it was and began thinking out loud. "Well," he said, "Don't panic now. All you have to do is understand the river. She's flowing around this bend down ahead and at the rate of speed she's going, I would have to say that if we run down the bank we can find just where the pup will come out!" So we ran and when we got down around the bend, Dad stood there for just a few seconds in complete silence. He looked over in the direction of the river, and the speed of the current and took into consideration the veg-etation and then walked to a certain spot on the ice and began chipping away and finally got down on his knees and hurriedly cleared away the ice chips. "Start calling her," he said. "If she hears you, she will keep trying!" We all started calling to her but a small part of myself felt all was lost. That was until up she came out from under the ice, right in the spot that Dad had predicted. Still on his knees, he scooped her out of the water and stuck her in my coat. I was wet with the river and wet with tears.

Dad took us home so the pup wouldn't get sick, but to this day I stand in awe of his ability to read the river like that. How he knew the pup would come up in that exact spot has always amazed me. I hope I will understand the river like that one day.

CHAPTER TWENTY-ONE

Moonlight Skating

By the culprits

WHEN WINTER COMES to the river bottoms, and the swamps freeze over, it's time to get out the ice skates. If the water level has been high when the hard freeze comes, sometimes the ice will be smooth as glass and just right for great skating If there have been strong winds or a heavy snowfall during the freezing period, however, the ice will be rough and uneven. The right conditions bring miles and miles of great skating or sledding until the winter snows cover everything.

The only hazard are the patches of tall grasses growing up here and there through the ice. During the day you can skate around them easily, but at night they are harder to see. There is a chance that you will take a bad fall if you skate over an unnoticed rock or a patch of grass.

After a hard freeze, our favorite place to spend our after-school hours was out in the swamps. Sometimes we would have to shovel skating paths if snow had covered the smooth ice.

The most fun was night skating during a full moon, when the ice was clear. Moonlight skating out in the swamps, with all of our brothers and sisters and our parents, is a great memory. How we would love it if we could all go back and do that one more time.

Dad would gather a big pile of brush to make a bonfire to keep us warm. We took wieners and marshmallows with us. Dad cut willow sticks for us with the trusty jackknife that he always carried in his pocket. He would sharpen one end of the sticks and give us all kinds of warnings about not poking ourselves or someone else with them.

After the fire was going good and everyone got their skates on, we would skate out into the night with the moon showing us the way. We always had to keep the fire in sight and keep a close watch on each other so that no one skated too far and got lost. The ice went on and on, so it was easy to get separated. Getting lost on a cold night was not a pleasant thought, even though we were all bundled up warm.

After skating for a long while, everyone would be hungry. Mom always brought along hot dogs, buns, and catsup, a big jug of hot vanilla cocoa, and a tin cup for each of us. We would all sit around the bonfire and roast the wieners and plunge our roasted marshmallows into our big tin cups of hot cocoa.

Dad kind of liked something else to keep him warm. I remember one time he had a bottle of Solomon Brothers wine. He poured the sweet purple wine into his tin cup and after he roasted his marshmallow, he dipped it into the wine before eating it. He was eating quite a few roasted marshmallows that night, so one of us asked him what it tasted like. He let each of us try one, and it was delicious. The sweet wine made the marshmallows so much better—even better than the hot vanilla cocoa. Our parents always let us have a sip of wine at Christmas or on some very special occasion. They didn't consider that this was one of those occasions, however.

After a while Dad set his cup of wine down and started skating with Mom. Some of us saw that as an opportunity to roast more marshmallows as fast as we could and soak them in Dad's wine. I guess we didn't think he would notice a little missing, since there wasn't much light. Before long, most of the wine in the cup had disappeared, so we refilled his tin cup from the bottle. Then we decided to bypass the roasting part and started dunking uncooked marshmallows into his wine cup. Little did we know that uncooked marshmallows soaked up more of the wine than the roasted ones. The big purple marshmallows looked almost as dark as if they had been roasted. Before long, all of the marshmallows had disappeared. So we refilled Dad's wine cup and tried to act real innocent.

We were glad that Dad and Mom were having a good time skating and weren't paying much attention to us. It wasn't long before Mom asked us why we weren't up skating. We told her that we were still resting from our earlier workout.

All of us were just sitting there around the campfire, having ourselves a fine time talking about our teachers and acting out little skits about them. As we recall, Casey was always the best at skits. She was showing us how her heavyset teacher had to turn sideways to get through the classroom door. Casey was rolling her hips as she took side-ways steps through a make-believe door. She looked so funny that we were laughing our heads off. At that point skating was the last thing on our minds. We were wishing that we had more marshmallows.

When our folks finally got tired, they skated back to the campfire only to find a whole lot of very happy kids, and not much wine left. All of a sudden the skating party was over. All of the supplies were loaded into the car. Off came our skates, and the bonfire was snuffed out. No one said much about what had happened, but that was one memorable ride home with all of us singing and each of us trying to outdo the other with our jokes. Mom and Dad were strangely silent on the ride.

We didn't realize until the next day that we had gotten a bit tipsy on marshmallows the night before. We didn't know if it was the strange combination or what. Those marshmallows sure packed a wallop, but did they ever taste good.

We often thought of doing that again, just to see if marshmallows are really as good as we had remembered on that one special night when we went moonlight skating out in the river bottoms.

There were more skating parties after that, and Mom always brought along hot vanilla cocoa and tin cups, but Dad never brought any Solomon Brothers wine along again. He probably wanted to spend his time skating and not watching what was happening to the marshmallows.

CHAPTER TWENTY-TWO

Chewing Tobacco and Hunting Deer

Robin Chamberlain Transo

I REMEMBER IT as clearly as if it had happened yesterday. Pete was thirteen years old and I was sixteen. It was the best kind of deer hunting weather possible because there was a chill in the air, but there wasn't any snow to have to trudge through. Snow is great for tracking a deer, but if it's deep, it means hard walking.

Dad had gone through the "new guy" training session with Pete the night before and, of course, reviewed all the hunting rules with the rest of us.

We were all up early the day the season opened. We went next door to the little restaurant that Bea Faulkner and her family operated. All the local hunters congregated there before going out on the hunt.

To me it was like being included into a secret society with all the other deer hunters, but to Pete it was like a rite of passage into young manhood.

Excitement ran high for all the deer hunters as they shared stories and drank coffee. Dad bought candy bars and chewing tobacco and then we all piled into the swamp buggy that Dad had made from an old car. We had our guns, hot cocoa, and sandwiches, and plenty of coffee in the thermos jugs to take the chill off the morning.

I don't know how many of us packed into the swamp buggy. It was the only way we could get up into the bottoms over the rough roads to Feather Island. Dad had gone out the day before and repaired the road so we would be able to get through. Other hunters would have to walk in, but that ugly old swamp buggy could go anyplace.

We went up the road until we got as close as possible to Feather Island. Pete and I carried the food to the place where we were going to make our deer stand. Dad had shown us the general area and we found a great spot there. Pete positioned himself about fifty yards to the southwest of me. He stood at one edge of a clearing and I stood at the other. Between us there was tall golden grass which changed color to ochre as the sun began edging its way up from behind the hills. There was a willow thicket between us and Feather Island.

Dad told us that the deer would be coming from that direction. "I want you to keep an eye on those willows because when the hunters start shooting across the river, the deer will come out of the hills, swim the river, cut across the head end of Feather Island, and come through these thickets right at you."

We waited and watched as dawn became morning. We sat there keeping an eye on each other and on the thicket while we chewed and spit tobacco as if we were grownups.

All of a sudden, shooting started in the hills, just as Dad had said it would. Soon, a young buck sprang from the thicket. Pete raised his gun and fired once. The deer went down. There was no movement in the clearing, so I motioned to Pete that there might be another one coming and that we should wait and keep quiet. We waited about five minutes. Then I thought we could move, so I started to walk through the clearing. Pete ran to his deer. It was dead. He started tagging him and gutting him out.

I felt in my bones that there was another deer out there but I wasn't sure whether I should leave Pete. He was so excited and he had all that mess to clean up, so I stood there for a while staring into the thickets, and then it happened. Out lunged a spike buck right at me. I fell back and fired the gun as I fell, shooting the deer in the underbelly. He veered off to the left and fell. I had to put him down with a second shot.

With all the shooting, it wasn't long before Dad and some of the rest of the family came running to see what was going on.

Pete was on his knees, cleaning out his deer like a pro when Dad came up to him. Pete was so proud, a big grin on his face. Dad said, "Good job there, Pete," as if Pete had been doing this sort of thing for years.

Then he came over to me and saw that I had gut-shot my deer. What a mess! Then he said to me, "How in God's name did you manage to get him at that angle?" "Well, Dad," I said, "it was either him or me and I just decided it was going to have to be him."

Of all the things that Pete and I have ever gone through, that day will be forever in my mind as my favorite memory.

Dad bragged for years about the time two of his kids came out of the woods with two deer that they shot the first half hour after deer season opened.

The next morning at the restaurant, the coffee flowed and the deer hunters looked at both of us as though we were right in there with the big boys. Someone even offered me a chew of tobacco. I looked at Dad and he just smiled as though to say, "It's your call." I winked at Pete and we bit off a big chew of plug tobacco.

CHAPTER TWENTY-THREE

A Little School

ICS WERE THE school initials and they had great meaning to all the children. I believe every child who ever went there had a special sense of pride in the little school. Those three letters will conjure up both happy and sad memories for the rest of their lives.

I think that part of that pride came from the fact that they felt they belonged to all the other children who went there—those before them, with them, and after them. As they put it when they were young, " We are the Catholics and they are the Publics," referring to the children who went to the other school in town. That wasn't a nice way of putting it, but it did say that they felt a bond among themselves and a special sense of belonging to their school.

A sadness comes over all of us when we think about the school being closed. Now there are no more happy shouts in the schoolyard while the children play "work up" or "tag." No more kick-the-can, hopscotch, or "red rover, red rover," no more "Captain may I," and "Pump-pump-pull-away." No more marbles, or jacks, or the dozens of other games that children played in that schoolyard. All gone now, traded for computer games and organized sports—and organized childhood.

The other day I overheard one of my children say how they wished they could win the lottery or meet some considerate rich person who was looking for an investment. He said, "I'd go back and renovate that school and put things back the way they were when we went to school there."

I didn't want to tell him that you can't go back. I didn't want to say that those things may be all but gone from the American scene forever. That they have been replaced by action movies and computerized videos that depict war, killing, and rape, savagery, conquering, sex, and generalized thuggery, which is far more exciting to many young people than, "Don't You Let the Old Witch Get My Children."

I didn't want to tell him that all of this has happened since the Catholic Church abandoned their little schools to the world of "What's Happening Now." I didn't say that as parents we have become complacent about helping the church maintain the small schools that used to dot our nation's small towns and cities. I didn't say those things, but I felt them deep in the heart of my soul. It's hard to walk past the little abandoned school that held only four classrooms without shedding a tear, not so much for the school, but for all the children who will never get a chance to go there.

Oh, there were things wrong with the school from time to time, like the nun who made a child stand in front of the class and wet on himself instead of listening to his pleas to go to the toilet. Those things happened in all schools. Those were issues that, as parents, we dealt with and helped the child restore his self-esteem.

Many would agree that the lay teachers brought a freshness and compassion to the school. Teachers like Rose Poole, who realized that a child who is comfortable can learn more, and more quickly, even if it meant permitting that child to lie on the floor by his desk. Of course, she first tried almost everything she could think of to keep him upright, but eventually realized that when he assumed that position he was so enthused and interested in his history book that nothing else mattered.

This wonderful teacher realized that one rule does not fit everyone.

Is it any wonder that she is remembered by the children as one of the best teachers they ever had?

All of our children who went to that school, and Dace himself, had many good memories, and some that were not so good. They all entered their adulthood with a great sense of pride that they had attended the Immaculate Conception School.

CHAPTER TWENTY-FOUR

The Trap Line

By Crystal "Crink" Chamberlain Hauck

"WHO WANTS TO go with me to pull my traps?" Dad asked. It was the last day of trapping season and he wanted some company on the trap line.

"I want to go," I told him, so I dressed in warm clothes and put on my boots. He didn't have to tell me that it was a long walk. I had been on the trap line with him enough times to know that it would be hours before we would get back. Today was going to be especially hard since we had to haul all of his traps back home.

Dad had mounted a big wooden box on a sled. He would tow the sled behind him with a rope he tied around his waist. That way he could walk through the ice and snow and have his hands free to check the traps.

When he went trapping, Dad always carried what he called his "tunkin-stick." The tunkin-stick was of good size and one of its uses was to test the strength of the ice. He had mounted a #3 catfish hook on the end of it, and he used it to reach down and pull the traps up out of the runs. If he found a muskrat in the trap, he would take it out of the trap, throw it in the box on the sled, reset the trap, and ease it back into the muskrat run. Then he would move on to the next set.

The tunkin-stick had other uses as well. If an animal in a trap wasn't quite dead, Dad would 'tunk' it on the head and put it out of its misery. I guess that's how his stick got its name. As long as I can remember, he had that stick with him whenever he went out on the trap line. In later years, I think that he probably used it to steady himself as he walked along.

Dad was a great teacher. He would always be teaching us something new as we walked the trap line. Different animals were trapped in different ways. If he were making a beaver set, he would cut down a sapling, one with a trunk about as big around as my wrist. He would trim off all the branches and mount a board at an angle about two or three feet from the bottom and then take his hatchet and sharpen the bottom of the pole. Then he would mount a trap on the board. He would run wire from the trap up to the top of the pole, which was approximately eight or ten feet long, and secure the wire to the pole. Above the mounted trap he would tie a bunch of tender young red willow shoots. He would gently ease the contraption down into the water run next to a beaver lodge and push it down into the mud. This was considered a humane set since the beaver would be caught under water and would not have to suffer long.

A muskrat set was also made to work underwater, but would be positioned in the runs, which are like little underwater canals between the muskrat houses. Dad always used Connibear traps which were the instant-kill trap. Fox, mink, otter, and raccoon trapping is not as humane as beaver and muskrat trapping. These sets are not usually drowning sets.

On the day that Dad and I pulled the traps, I was given the job of pulling the sled. That day Dad had a five-gallon pail on the sled that he put beside the wooden box. He would pull a trap, throw it into the box, and put any furs he got into the pail.

After we got all the muskrat traps pulled, we went on to run his otter traps. We started out checking and pulling traps as we went. We came to this one set and were thrilled to find that Dad had caught an otter in it. It was a rare experience to trap an otter, not because they were scarce, but because they were so difficult to catch. What a joy it was for him to finish off the season with an otter to his credit. Dad and I were jumping around like we were celebrating a great occasion. We were so excited.

We talked and talked as we went along pulling up the last of the traps. We had one left to pull and then we could go home and show everyone the otter. When we got to the last trap, we were dumfounded to find that he had caught another otter. We could not believe our eyes. Dad had been so thrilled with the first one, but you should have seen him then. He couldn't believe he had caught two of them in the same day. He was so excited he didn't know what to do. None of the trappers in the area were going to believe this. I have never seen my dad so happy. When we got home, he was showing off those otters to everyone.

Dad always let Joe and Casey and me skin out the muskrat, and he would skin and stretch the more expensive furs such as the beaver or the raccoon when they brought a good price. He never wasted anything. He would take the muskrat carcasses and use them for bait for his mink and fox sets.

Dad let everyone know that no one was going to skin the otters but the two of us. I was allowed to hold them while he skinned them out. He took such pains removing the fur and stretching it and fleshing it out. After they were dried, he sent them out to be tanned. One of the pelts was 63½ inches long from nose to the tip of the tail, and the other was 64 inches.

Trapping those two otters was an experience that he talked about for years. None of the other trappers in the area could top that, and they probably would not have believed him if he hadn't had the snapshots to prove it.

A Hard Lesson

I had a wrist rocket one time, and I went out behind the house and got some rocks and started shooting at two little bullheads that were stuck together. I killed them both in one shot, and thought, "Wow! This is really something. Dad is going to be so proud of me because of my aim." I ran into the house and said, "Dad, Dad, look what I did," and I showed him the bullheads and told him how I got them. He looked at me and said, "You're pretty proud of yourself, aren't you?"

I said, "Yeh, it was a real neat shot."

Then he said, "Is that what I taught you?" I was confused. Again he said, "Is that what I taught you? Did I teach you to kill, just to kill?" He went on to say that he was teaching us to hunt and to trap but that it was for survival, not just to kill an animal for the sake of killing. He said he wasn't teaching us a sport but was teaching us how to use what God had given us for a living. Needless to say, when he was finished with me, I felt about two inches tall. That was a good message for me, from Dad, a lesson I have never forgotten.

CHAPTER TWENTY-FIVE

My First Hunt

By Casey Chamberlain

NOVEMBER 1972 WAS my first year to go deer hunting. I had been waiting forever, it seemed, for my chance to go with the rest of the hunting party. They left the house early on opening day, and every day after that for a week until the hunt was over. Until then, all I could do was to sit at the window with Crink and Joe and wait until the hunters came back. When we saw the truck pull in, we would run out to see if anyone got anything.

The night before opening day, we all sat around the big table while Dad laid out the plan for the next day's hunt. I listened to him intently as he explained to the whole hunting party just how each drive would be conducted.

"You will all start at Prairie du Bay and drive to the gut first, where I'll be on stand," he said, "then we'll meet up and I'll go on down to the head-end of Feather Island and you will drive from the gut to the sandbar. We'll meet up again and I'll go on down to the lower end of Feather Island. From there we'll drive Willow and Kroll Islands and then to the main bank and we'll end up at the cabin."

Then he said, "For all of you who haven't hunted with us before, the rules are strict and you'll follow them or you'll never hunt with us again. That means you will all line up across the bottoms. You must always keep the person on both sides of you in sight at all times. If you

are the last person toward the swamps or the one next to the river, you only have one person to keep in sight. Keep the line straight and whoop all the way. No shooting at anything but deer. Now remember that you must never, never, shoot behind yourself or behind anyone else, nor to either side of yourself. You can only shoot straight ahead during a drive. That way no one will get hurt."

I was so excited! Watching Dad and seeing how everyone was listening to him and agreeing with what he said, made me feel so proud that he was my dad. He seemed so powerful and in charge of everything.

Every year after the plans for the following day were clear in everyone's mind, it was time to tell stories about hunts of earlier years. Dad always told the ones about "Old Slew Foot," the swamp buck so old that he was almost black. He was called Slew Foot because one of his front feet was either deformed or had been injured. You could always tell his track. One half of his front hoof jutted out at an angle. Slew Foot had eluded Dad for years. The first thing Dad looked for each season, when he found any deer signs, was to see whether that big old telltale deer track was there. When he would see it, the hunt for Slew Foot began. How Dad wanted to bag that old buck! It seemed that he always got to shoot at him but never hit him, even though Dad was the best shot around. Once he said that he hoped he never would get him, because half the fun of hunting would be gone without Slew Foot out there to lend that special excitement to the hunt. We never did hear of anyone shooting him. He probably just died from old age, or maybe he's still out there just waiting for Dad.

Part of me felt a sadness, thinking of Joe and Crink sitting there by the window anxiously waiting for us to come in from the hunt. It made me even more determined to get a deer so they wouldn't be disappointed.

When story time ended and everyone left for the night, Dad asked me if I wanted to help make the sandwiches and get the food together for the next day. Of course I was totally ready to do anything and everything that involved the big hunt, so I jumped at the chance. I always wondered why the older ones didn't seem to want to help with that aspect of the preparations, but after years of making sandwiches I began to appreciate their reluctance.

After the food was fixed, Dad gave me the 12-gauge shotgun that I would be using. He went over all the features of the gun and made me show him how the safety worked and how to reload it after I had fired a shot. He made me go over and over the lesson until he felt comfortable with my using the gun. I didn't want to tell him but the gun felt too long and was too heavy. I wanted him to think that I could handle it. It was late when we finished so he told me to get to bed and get some sleep so I would be ready to go in the morning.

I was so excited, I had a hard time sleeping. I could just picture old Slew Foot running in front of me and my shooting him and thinking how proud Dad would be of me.

It didn't seem as if I was asleep very long when I heard Dad hollering for everyone to get up and get ready to go. I couldn't move fast enough! Mom was making bacon, eggs, hash browns, and toast for breakfast. The house smelled so good. Everyone was up eating and getting dressed in their hunting gear.

I was running around getting my 12-gauge shells together, then checking , double-checking, and triple-checking my back tag to be sure it was fastened properly on my coat. Dad was so calm, everything just fell into place for him, while I was running around like a chicken with its head cut off. As years went by, I understood that the calmness came with experience.

Just before we started out the door, we all got Mom's annual lecture on safety. How a gun was always loaded even when it didn't have any shells in it and therefore must never be pointed at anyone! How the gun must always be pointed toward the ground except when firing. How, if we messed up, she would tell us in a loud clear voice in front of anyone and everyone and we might not get to go out again until we learned that lesson. Then she would give each of us a good-luck kiss on the forehead. It was all so cool.

We arrived at Prairie du Bay before the sun came up. I remember thinking to myself, "What if I get lost? What if I accidentally shoot someone?" Yipes!!!

We got out of the vehicles and loaded our weapons and Dad started telling everyone how they would line up for the drive. I, being the rookie, was told to stay next to the riverbank and Mom would be on the road to my left.

Dad asked us to give him a little time to walk quietly down to the gut, which was almost a mile below where we were going into the bottoms. That way he could get himself positioned on a stand and we were then to drive the deer towards him. He was in the best spot, but then he

was the best shot. I always felt a little sorry that he missed the fun of
the drive itself. The older hunters in the party knew just about how long
it would take him to get there and be ready for us to start the drive. Once
again, *experience!*

The first drive of the morning involved at least twenty relatives and
several friends, and as we started down through the river bottoms we
began whooping and hollering in high-pitched voices, just as Dad had
instructed. Sometimes I was concentrating on the whooping and hollering more than on the hunting because I was worried that I might not
be doing it right. Everyone was looking from side to side to make sure
that we were lined up the way we were supposed to be, and then they
looked to the front for any signs of deer.

We knew that no other hunters would be ahead of us. Everyone
always knew how we run the drives every year, so no one hunted in that
area. Other hunters would position themselves around the outside edge
of the swamps or on the banks along Prairie du Bay, hoping that we
would kick something up to them, but they weren't about to go into the
bottoms during a Chamberlain drive.

I don't remember if anyone got anything on the first leg of the drive
but I do remember shots being fired. When I heard them, I freaked out

and hit the ground. Of course, Mom had made us promise to do this, and I have always kept that promise to this day.

When we got to the gut, Dad was standing there looking so cool. Reaching Dad at the end of a drive was for me the most enjoyable part of the hunt. Everyone would gather around and we'd all be telling jokes and laughing at all the tall stories, such as my cousin Stacey's tales about the twelve-point buck she had just seen on the drive. We figured that if she had time to stop and count the points, she should have had time to shoot him. Then we really would have had something to talk about. The fun we had at the stops between drives was worth all the briar cuts we got as we struggled through the thickets.

After we laughed and talked for a while, Dad explained the next phase of the drive. Now we were to drive from the gut to the upper end of Feather Island. I felt so good to have the first part of the drive under my belt. I still felt awkward with that 12-gauge. It was so heavy that my arms were killing me. Dad gave me a big hug and I can't even describe how that made me feel in front of all those hunters who saw him as The King of Hunting.

Dad went on again and got in position while we waited. Then we lined up again and I was assigned once more to the riverbank. Years later, when I would have to work the middle area of the drives and work my way through the dense thickets, I would think back and remember how nice it was to get to work the riverbank.

On this part of the drive, everyone was as loud as before. As I walked along, I wondered what I would do if I saw a deer swimming in the river. Should I shoot him? Was it legal? It worried me because I remembered being told that it wasn't safe to fire a gun at water. The second part of the drive seemed to go more quickly. Then I saw Dad up ahead sitting up against a tree, waving at us. What a welcome sight. Once again, we discussed what we had seen and once again cousin Stacey had seen another twelve-pointer. The laughs we have had over the years from her buck stories are priceless. She is always totally serious when she tells them.

The main part of the drive was now in front of me. Feather Island was up ahead. I had heard my family talking about hunting at Feather Island for years, and now at last I was going to be hunting here, myself. My heart was pounding so loudly it seemed as if I could hear it. I didn't even feel any pain in my arms now from the heavy shotgun. We lined up at the head-end and waited for Dad to get at the lower end and find a spot to stand. I can't even remember who was on the stand with him, nor did it matter to me. All I knew was that I wasn't cold anymore and I was ready to get Old Slew Foot.

My brother Peter was on one side of me and Mom was on the other as we started down the long island. Everyone else was fanned out across the island. Pete could see that I was enjoying myself by the big smile on my face. By then I was holding the shotgun as if I were a soldier.

We worked our way down the island and were finally almost to the end when I heard someone yelling that there was a deer heading my way. Then there it was, crossing right in front of me. I'm sure I stopped breathing. Then I heard Pete yell, "Shoot! Case! Shoot!"

I just remember firing the gun and pumping it as fast as I could and shooting again. I don't know how many shots I fired. Then I heard Pete yelling, "You got him! Good shot, Case!" I felt as if I were in a daze, or that I was dreaming.

Everyone gathered around the deer and I remember Dad crouching down and lifting its head. He looked up at me and said, "Hey, you got a nubbin buck. I'll be damned." That didn't really mean much to me. I was just overwhelmed at the whole situation and had no idea what to do next.

Of course, Dad didn't waste any time telling me. "Well, gut it out, Case. You shot it."

I just looked at him and said, "OK, sure." I had no idea how to field-dress a deer. It seemed as if Dad thought I should just know intuitively since I was now a hunter. I didn't want him to think for one minute that I was clueless.

I knelt down and watched every one of them walk away from me towards Willow Island. I felt sad and scared, now that I was alone, and I didn't want to be embarrassed because I didn't know what I was doing. Just then, Pete came back and knelt down next to me and said, "Don't worry, Case, I'll help you—but don't tell Dad." Man, was I relieved. I was fascinated with what Pete was teaching me about field-dressing the deer.

I did find out from Dad, later, that he would not have left me to do it by myself. I should have known that Mom wouldn't have either, but at the moment I felt abandoned, until Pete came and showed me what to do. I guess this was a trick that they played on the rookies. It would make for good listening at next year's story time.

So many memorable things happened that day. One of them was the ride home. I was barely able to contain myself when we pulled up into the driveway. I jumped out of the car so fast and ran into the house to tell Crink and Joe. I have always felt that the deer belonged to the three of us because I knew how excited they were for me.

Dad and Peter took me to register the deer and Dad acted so proud of me. He was telling everyone that I got it with one shot. Well, I shot quite a few times. Maybe only one shot did hit him, but it sounded so much better the way Dad told it.

I went deer hunting every year after that. Whenever I come to that spot on Feather Island I always smile and remember my first hunt, and my brother Peter, and my dad.

The two of them are probably out there together somewhere right now, tracking down old Slew Foot and having some great times doing it. When my time here is over, I'll join them and it will be just like old times again.

CHAPTER TWENTY-SIX

Remembering Dad

Glimpses by the family

Mark

Dad and I went hunting one day in the back swamps. Dad shot a duck and went out to get it. The water was only about a foot deep but the muck under it was over three feet deep. Dad quickly sank up to his waist in the mire. I helped get him out by grabbing onto his shotgun and pulling. When he was finally free, he said, "No duck is worth this much trouble." So we left and started back home. We agreed that a dog would have been a big help in this situation.

On the way home he let me use the 12-gauge shotgun to shoot a squirrel that was in a tree. He told me to aim for the head since I was so close to it. I did, but just as I squeezed the trigger the squirrel turned and ran toward me and the blast blew him apart. About the only thing left was the tail. I felt awful, but Dad's sense of humor took over. He told me about the only thing we could do with what was left of the squirrel was to sell it to Buckhorn Fur Center in Richland Center. He said they might give me a dime for the tail and it could be used to make a Mepps lure, since that was all it was good for. Needless to say, it wasn't a very productive day of hunting for either of us.

I remember a time when we were with Dad when he was hunting pheasants up at Prairie du Bay. Dad had shot a pheasant and the high school biology teacher's dog ran away with it. Dad was so angry that he could have shot that dog. He told the dog's owner that mad dogs like his, who destroy game, are impounded by the DNR and put to sleep. I don't think the teacher liked that comment very much, since he took such pride in his purebred hunting dog.

Mike

I don't know anyone but Dace Chamberlain who would cut the top off of a car, remove the doors, and make it into a swamp buggy, but he did, and it was quite a vehicle. It was a Buick Wildcat 440 with a powerful engine.

One time when we were out in the swamps we passed a four-wheel drive vehicle that was stuck in the ruts in the old road to Feather Island. Boy, did those guys give us some looks, but hey, we were moving and they weren't.

When Dad removed the doors from the Buick, he left the hinges on the frame. We would swing open a door hinge and brace our foot on it. It was sort of like having your foot in a stirrup. It was best to brace yourself with your foot on the top hinge. You felt kind of cool, too, riding along with your leg cocked up like that. Like that's how you were supposed to look and nobody else knew it yet. Anyway, we would take off out through the swamps and through the tall grass and never have any idea what kind of ground we were driving over. When Dad gunned the engine, the mud flew ten feet in the air.

Mom was always embarrassed when we loaded up in that car and headed out of town. She said we looked like the Beverly Hillbillies. When we came back she really had something to be embarrassed about, because then we would be covered with mud.

We went rock hunting lots of times with Dad. Working over a big pile of rocks looking for agates was always fun. When you'd find one, it didn't matter if it was a big one or a small one, Dad got just as excited over it as you did. The first thing he would do is spit on it, so he could see the lines in the agate. He had this sprayer that he would sometimes use to wet down the pile of rocks. Then it was easy to see which ones were the agates.

I remember he had a rock polisher that ran all the time. I don't think he ever made any jewelry or anything out of the rocks. He just enjoyed polishing them until they were all smooth and shiny.

Dad knew the names of every rock we picked up. He studied several rock books that he owned, so he became the family expert. We kids knew the different kinds of agates—the conglomerates, rare bullseye, water agates, moss agates, and others—but we had to ask him to identify most

of the other specimens we found. He would look the rock over and usually could tell us what kind it was.

Then it seemed as though he started calling a lot of different rocks
leaverite. Many of these rocks looked really different from each other,
so we kind of wondered about his expertise. We decided to search
through the rock books ourselves. We couldn't find anything. We went
back to Dad and told him that there wasn't anything about leaverite that
we could find, and asked him why he was calling all the different kinds
of rocks by that name.

"Oh," he said, "you aren't going to find leaverite in the rock books.
That's just the name for any rock that's not worth picking up. It means
'leave 'er right' where you found it."

After that everything was either an agate or a leaverite.

Rock

I remember a rope-making machine that Dad made. I don't know if
he saw one somewhere and copied the idea, or if he invented the thing
himself. I can believe that he invented it, since he was always coming
up with something that no one else ever thought of. Anyway, he made
this thing that took two people to operate. The person standing a few
feet in front of him would hold this board that had six eye hooks screwed
into it. Through each eye hook he would run a string of binding twine.
Each string of twine ran to its own individual roll of twine. Dad would
take each of the strings of twine and hook them up somehow to a board
in his hand that had three eye hooks and a handle.

When he turned the handle, the strings were pulled through the eyes
on the board you were holding and into the eyes on the board he was
holding, and out the other side would come the rope. It was a real rope.
There were no loose strings of twine anywhere to be seen. I have never
figured out how he did that, but it was sure a lot of fun helping him make
rope with his homemade machine.

Joe

Dad plowed the fields on our land with an old 1941 John Deere B
that Mom bought. It was made before World War II and it could run on
either gasoline or kerosene. After he plowed he would disk and then
drag the fields. It was up to us kids to pick up the rocks that worked up

to the top of the ground. That was a terrible job. We didn't mind picking them off the field so much as we hated carrying them to a rock pile in the middle of the field or carrying a load of them off to the side. Even though the fields were only about an acre in size, it still meant a lot of rock carrying.

Dad solved the problem by building an old-fashioned sled, which we called a stone boat. He took two logs, about ten or twelve feet long, and trimmed the front of each one so that it had the shape of a sled runner. Then he set the log runners about six feet apart, parallel, and nailed planks crosswise, to make a sled. He hooked a chain to each of the log runners and then hooked the other end to the back of the tractor. When he pulled the stone boat through the field, we actually had fun loading it up. When it was full of rocks he would drive to the ditch at the end of the field, go up the bank on the other side, and all the rocks would roll out. Then he would circle back for another load.

When all the rocks were cleared off the fields, we used the stone boat for rides. Everyone would pile on and sit back-to-back at the center of the sled. He made us cross our legs so that no one had a foot out that could get run over, and then he would pull all of us up the old hill road. There we'd go, with our butts not a foot from the ground, riding over the rocky road, checking out the ferns and wild flowers and looking for morel mushrooms. We used to have a lot of weekend visitors to the land in those days. They always brought all their kids for a stone boat ride. I remember Dad would have to make four or five trips on a Sunday afternoon, up to the top of the hill and back just to make sure that everyone, adults and kids alike, got a ride on the stone boat.

Mark

We had a great big rock in our side yard that we couldn't move. The thing was always in the way and our folks were afraid we would trip and fall against it and get hurt. It was about four feet in diameter and it stood a couple of feet out of the ground.

After our little sister, Francine, died, we were all having a difficult time dealing with the grief. Dad thought that we should build a small shrine in memory of her, so he decided to put a water fountain on top of the rock.

He got old broken silo staves and built a structure by laying them flat with the formed end of the stave facing outward. He put cement between the staves. The shrine stood about six feet high when it was finished, which included the height of the rock that it stood on. When he finished the shrine, it looked like a castle from King Arthur's time. On the backside of the shrine he put a half-inch metal pipe that ran from the bottom to the top.

The top of the castle was actually a birdbath, so when he hooked up a hose to the metal pipe in the back, the water would shoot into the air and come down into the birdbath and then flow down over the sides of the castle walls.

There was a recessed area built into the front of the castle where he placed a three-foot statue of the Blessed Mother and another of St. Francis of Assisi, standing side by side. The recessed area, or little room, was big enough so that when the water came down over the sides of the castle, the statues didn't get wet.

Around the castle Dad built a moat from silo staves. He made the moat a little more than a foot wide and about a foot deep. The inside wall of the moat was the big rock itself. The moat, like the castle, had no regular shape. It simply followed the contour of the rock that he was trying to hide. When the outside stave wall was finished, he poured a cement floor in the bottom of the moat so that it would hold water. He put a smooth finish on the floor and then allowed the cement to dry for several days.

Everyone in the family could hardly wait for the cement to cure. We all wanted to see the fountain in operation. The time finally came and we all gathered around to watch. The late afternoon sun was just sinking below the treetops when Dad turned on the water to the fountain. The sun struck the cascading water and reflected its light. The most beautiful rainbow colors appeared all around us. I think we all thought that was a sign that Francine was safe in the arms of Jesus.

After a while, Dad said, "Come on, we're going down to the river and seine some fish for the shrine." When we came back we had about fifty small fish in the five-gallon bucket. I think we had some of almost every kind of fish that lived in the river. None of them was more than three inches long. Some were illegal to seine, but we brought them home, anyway.

The shrine came alive when we put the fish in the moat. They swam all the way around the castle. Round and round they went. We watched them until dark and then we went in the house and got some candles, lit them, and put them in the little room beside the Blessed Mother and St. Francis.

We sat there for long time that night. We were so grateful to Dad for building us the shrine that we thanked him over and over again.

In the years that followed, we spent a lot of time around the shrine. It was always the center of attraction in the yard. When anyone graduated from high school and had a party, it was always held around the shrine.

It was thirty years ago that Dad built the shrine. The ground shifting in winter has caused the moat to leak, and we have repaired it from time to time. The fountain still works. The castle still stands on the rock, and the same two statues still stand there, side by side.

Rock

I'll never forget the time Dad and I went pheasant hunting at Prairie du Bay. There was a group of teachers who belonged to the Rod and Gun Club hunting with their purebred bird dogs. Dad had once had words with one of them when the teacher's dog ran off with Dad's bird after he had shot him. Some of the other Rod and Gun Club members were not too friendly with him, anyway, ever since a controversy over their use of a road and boat landing that Dad had built.

Anyway, Dad and I left there and decided we would go down near the old cabin site and look over the area to see where to put his muskrat traps when the season opened. We took our guns along but didn't expect to see any pheasants down there, since the DNR always set all the pheasants out in the Prairie du Bay area.

We were just about finished checking muskrat houses and otter runs along the road to Feather Island by the edge of the marsh, when in drove a DNR truck. Two men got out and asked us what we were doing there. Dad said, "I'm checking where I'll be making my muskrat sets. Why?"

"Oh," they said, "we were just going to let out some pheasants, but we didn't want to put them in the same place, since they hunt them out so fast up there," nodding toward Prairie du Bay. Dad knew that they meant the teachers. The DNR men acted kind of relieved. They didn't have to say any more.

Dad said, "No, I'm just checking where I'll be putting my traps. I should be through in about another hour or so."

They seemed satisfied with his answer, so they went ahead and released fifteen or twenty birds.

Dad's eyes were gleaming and there was a big smile on his face as he watched which direction the pheasants took off. When the DNR men finished, they got in their truck and left. As soon as they were back on the main highway and headed to town, Dad got the guns out of the truck and suddenly we were back pheasant hunting again. Needless to say, we went home with well over our bag limit. We had a pheasant feast that night. It sort of made up, in a way, for all the times the teachers had crowded the other hunters out.

I must have gone on the trap line a lot with Dad, because when I first went with him I would have to take three steps to every one of his. It seems like that went on for a long time, and then one day I realized I was taking only two steps to every one of his.

One day we were out running the trap line in the upper bottoms. We were walking along and talking about some otter signs we had just seen. He was telling me how he had trapped these two big otters and was showing me right where he had gotten them.

He was telling me about a reporter who wrote for the *Wisconsin State Journal* who said that there weren't any otter anymore in the lower Wisconsin River bottoms. We were laughing about this man's limited knowledge of the area. Dad said something about how the guy ought to get off his butt, get out of his office, and get down here, and we would show him whether or not there were otter here anymore. Dad said he was going to call the guy and tell him he didn't know what he was talking about.

As we walked along, I fell into stride behind Dad and I started stepping in his tracks as I walked. We walked quite a way and then Dad stopped and looked back. He noticed that there was only one set of tracks behind us. He looked right at me and said, "Well, Rock, I guess it's time that you and I become partners."

When we went home, I went uptown and bought some traps and got the license and tags. From then on Dad and I always trapped together.

Crink

Joe and Casey and I went northern fishing with Dad up by the Rice Pond. Dad brought the flat bottom boat along. He was fishing from the boat and we were fishing from the bank. There were hundreds of lily pads and cattails growing there and we couldn't always see Dad over the vegetation. All of a sudden he rowed back in to the bank and he seemed to be sort of upset. We asked him what was wrong and he said that he had had this great big northern on the line but he had lost him.

We just said, "Oh, sure, Dad, good story."

"No," he insisted, "I had him on and he was so big that he snapped my line and took my Johnson silver minnow." We knew that meant the end of fishing for the day because Dad couldn't fish without his silver minnow. When we got home he went uptown and got another one and some stronger line.

The next day we were back fishing at the Rice Pond. Dad got a strike and a good-size northern danced across the water on his tail like they do when you hook them good. It was a nice-size fish but Dad said it wasn't anywhere near as big as the one he had lost the day before. We kids just kind of grinned at each other, then all at once Dad had another strike. This fish looked to be a lot bigger than the first one. Dad set the hook and reeled him in. The fish was huge. Dad pulled him up into the boat and there in his lip was the Johnson silver minnow that he had lost the day before. Not only did he get the fish but he got his silver minnow back. After that, we weren't so quick to doubt Dad when he told us a story about fishing.

When I was in high school, we lived on the edge of town. I used to get up at 6:30 and make a two-mile run down to the bridge and back every morning. About halfway down, on the big bend, there would be Dad standing beside his truck, drinking a cup of coffee. I'd just wave to him as I went by but I'd never stop and talk or anything. I felt like it would be violating him, somehow, to do that. He'd be just standing there, looking to the east, watching the sun come up over the river bottoms. I wondered what he was thinking about. I never knew why he chose that spot to stand, but he could always see me on the full length of my run.

Mom

For the last thirty-five years of his life, Dace had a beard. He hated shaving, so when men started growing beards for deer season, that was a perfect excuse for him to grow one, as well. After deer season was over for a while, everyone else shaved their beards off, but he didn't. The first year that he let it grow, he said he just wanted to get a jump on everyone else for the next season. By the next year, his beard was long and brown. Women used to ask me, "Do you like that thing?" Rather than act embarrassed, which I was, I would say, "Oh yes, I think it's nice." As time went on I missed his face. I finally got used to the beard but I'd tell people, "I married Bing Crosby but I wound up with Gabby Hayes." Dace did look like Bing Crosby when he was young.

When he got older and his beard turned white, he gained more weight and he always wore glasses, so he began to look like Santa Claus. I wasn't the only one who thought so. One day when we were at West Towne Mall, a lady came up and asked him if he would consider playing Santa Claus for the mall at Christmastime. With a little rouge on his cheeks and a Santa Claus outfit, he took the job, and for years he was the mall's favorite Santa.

Some of his own kids had never seen him without the beard. One time, he shaved it off. When Joe saw him for the first time after he shaved, he called me and said he would never have known Dad if he had met him on the street. I think that it was kind of a shock for everyone. He kept the beard off for quite a while but then grew it back again. I guess he wanted to use up all that after-shave lotion he had gotten over the years as gifts. I really think that he wasn't ready to give up the Santa role, especially since he had spent over two hundred dollars on a tailor-made red velvet Santa Claus suit that he kept hidden away in his closet.

Casey

One summer day, on my day off, I drove down to Boscobel from River Falls to see how Dad was doing. I did this quite often when I had any free time because of my growing concern over his health.

When I pulled into the yard, there he was, working on something in the back of his old pickup truck. I'll never forget the look on his face when he looked up and saw me. He gave me a real long hug and told me he loved me. I said that I had come down to see him and he told me he was so glad I came. His eyes were glistening a little as he started to make suggestions about what we should do on such a beautiful day. I told him that I thought we should take the boat out and have a picnic somewhere on the river. He quickly agreed.

We went to Dick's supermarket in his old truck and got some soda and food for the picnic. Then we hooked the boat up to the truck and took our life jackets and picnic supplies and headed for the river.

On the way, I looked at him and I almost started to cry. I missed him and it was hard for me being away from him so much. I had been think- ing how hard life would be without him. I said, "Dad, I love you so much. I sure get lonesome for you sometimes." He looked at me with those big sad but happy eyes, and said again how glad he was that I had come down, and told me that he loved me, too.

We went down the cabin road and Dad backed the truck up while I eased the boat into the river. After he parked the truck, we got in the boat and started up the river.

We had gone a short way when he said, "Hey, do you want to drive the boat? It's about time you learn. If you don't, who's going to do it during deer hunting when I can't?" I was so excited. I had always wanted to learn but just never had the chance.

Dad moved over and let me sit next to him while he instructed me on all the do's and don'ts of boating. He warned me about all the things that were potential hazards. As we went up the river, we talked about anything and everything. The sun was warm and we were just having fun being together. When we got to the gut, we slowly inched our way into the backwaters as we checked for deer signs. When we got as far as we could go, I shut the motor off and we just sat there listening to the sounds of nature. Then we took out our food and started eating as we remembered deer hunting stories from the past and talked about plans for future hunts.

The mosquitoes finally drove us out, so we headed on up the river. Dad told me to always head upriver whenever I went boating. That way if the motor conks out, drifting back down to the landing would be so much easier than trying to row upstream against the current.

After a couple of hours we decided to go back. When we got home, I could tell that Dad was really tired. He lay down and we watched TV for a while and he dozed off. I went over and gave him a big hug and told him I loved him and that I would be back soon for our next adventure. He looked sad when I left but he told me that I had made his whole day for him.

This was a very special day for both of us and is now one of my favorite memories.

Mom

Dace used to chew tobacco and smoke cigarettes. It seemed as if he always had a chew in his mouth. Sometimes he was chewing and smoking at the same time. That was years before anyone knew how bad tobacco was for you, or considered someone a poor role model who used tobacco in front of young people. That was about the time that Dace was the cub master and his friend Bill Ware was scoutmaster for Troop 92 of the Boy Scouts.

One year, the two men took all the Scouts down to Canyon Camp near Apple River, Illinois, for a big pow-wow. They camped out for several days and on Saturday night there was to be an award ceremony for the boys who had achieved something outstanding during the previous year. One of the awards that they were hoping that some of the boys would win was the Order of the Arrow.

Scouts and leaders from all over the district were there, all of them full of anticipation that someone they knew might be tapped for the award. It was a rare occasion when a leader would be considered for the honor.

The ceremony started off with some of the Scouts performing Native American dances. The boys would dance around the fire and then go out among the Scouts and leaders, and when they came to someone who had been selected for the Order of the Arrow, they would hit him on the shoulder. That was called "tapping them out." The rules were that, if you were tapped out, you could not speak for twenty-four hours. You were led away from the campsite into the woods with only a slice of bread and a boiled egg and an axe. For the next full day you would not see another person, and you were given a work assignment. You had to sleep on the ground and you were not given anything to drink. You had no mosquito repellent, no extra clothing. Nothing!

The mothers and wives viewed this as pretty harsh, but to the men and the boys it represented a rite of passage.

Dace was standing by Bill Ware, chewing his tobacco, as they quietly speculated about which of their Scouts might get tapped out. The Scouts danced through the crowd and one of them came up from behind and hit Dace hard on the shoulder. He was so shocked and surprised that he swallowed his chew. At first it was kind of caught in his throat and then he managed to swallow it down, but of course now he couldn't get a drink to wash it down and he couldn't speak to anyone to tell them what happened. Worse yet, it would be twenty-four hours before he could get some water to clear his mouth and throat of the tobacco. He was led away into the woods without anyone knowing what had happened.

He never said much about the experience except to tell me he had gotten kind of sick. I noticed that he didn't chew for several years after he got the Order of the Arrow award.

Crink

It was always so great to be out deer hunting with Dad. I remember one time when I had the rare privilege of being on a stand with him. I usually was one of the drivers. We were waiting for the drive to start and Dad told me about a story he had read about a beaver that had found an old stovepipe that still had the flue attached to it. The beaver had built his dam so that all the water in this small creek went through the stovepipe and the beaver was able to regulate the flow of water in the creek by opening or closing the flue. While Dad was telling me the story, it started to snow. Just then a doe came running toward us. We just stood there and looked at her. It was such a great moment for me, being there with him and listening to his story as we enjoyed the snowfall and watched the deer run off through the woods.

Joe

In our family, no one had any special role. We were all expected to learn how to do things for ourselves. I remember Mom saying that the boys and girls alike had to learn how to sew on their own buttons and repair their own clothes, as well as wash and iron their own things.

By conventional standards, our parents' roles were often reversed. Mom grew up working in the fields and Dad grew up working with his sister in their restaurant. Mom always said that Dad had to teach her how to cook. She said that she hadn't known the difference between a pork roast and a beef roast until he taught her. There was always kind of a competition between them as to who was the better cook. Everything they fixed seemed to taste great to us kids.

In winter, when the seasonal work was finished for the year, the role of cooking often became Dad's responsibility, since Mom worked eight to ten shifts a week and was glad to come home to a good hot meal.

Dad would fix big pots of spaghetti, chili, stew, or soup for our dinner. Sometimes he would fix johnnycake to go along with it.

My favorite meal was his potato soup. He always put a lot of onions in it. Then he would fry a whole three-pound box of bacon ends until they were crisp, and crumble that up and put it into the pot. He would pour all of the bacon grease into the soup pot and mix it all up. After a while, he would skim off the clear grease and leave the flavor behind. When the potatoes and the onions were cooked, he would add cans and cans of whole condensed milk and bring the soup to the boiling point and shut off the heat. Then he would give it the final taste test to see that it had enough salt and pepper.

We kids would put the biggest bowls we could find on the table, but one bowl of Dad's soup was never enough. I think he must have put fifteen or twenty pounds of potatoes into a batch of that soup. There was always enough for that night and the next morning, too. Potato soup and cornbread make a great breakfast before going off to school on a cold winter morning.

On winter mornings when we didn't have to go to school, Casey, Crink, and I always went on the trap line with Dad. That meant several miles of walking, twice a day. We had so many great experiences out there with Dad. He would show us mink and fox signs and where the otters slid down the banks on their bellies while they played. As we walked along listening to him, we almost believed that he knew what the animals were thinking. He would show us where they marked their boundaries and how recently they visited a certain place. The urine or dung that they left was like a special message from them to him. Sometimes he would take a small bottle from his pocket and put a drop of lure on or near where the animal had left its markings.

Dad always ran his traps in the early morning and then again late in the afternoon. He told us that a good trapper checked his traps twice a day to prevent any unnecessary suffering of the animals. He often caught more than one muskrat in the same trap on the same day. That meant that Casey, Crink, and I had a lot of skinning to do.

Whether we went to school or out on the trap line, we had furs to skin at night. The first thing we did was to check our knives to make sure they were sharp. Dad showed us how to bring a razor sharpness to a knife by spitting on the whetstone and wiping the knife back and forth across it until the edge was just right.

Casey, Crink, and I were allowed to skin only the muskrats, while Dad and the older kids, Peter, Mark, and Rock, skinned the bigger animals. We'd sit around in a circle down in the basement as we worked. We would talk about what we saw that day or listen to Dad tell us what he had caught in each set, if we weren't along with him. We always had such a good time while we worked, and when we were finished he would check each pelt to make sure we hadn't put a cut in any of the fur. Dad wouldn't have been too happy with us if we hadn't been paying attention and had let the knife slip and cut a fur. It would have been a waste of an animal's life, as well as a loss of face for us, and a loss of money for the family. All the animal carcasses were saved and taken back out on the trap line to bait the next day's traps.

After the skinning was finished, Dad would stretch the pelts on boards of different sizes, depending upon the kind of animal it was. Then he would flesh out the fur, which meant he cut away any tissue or fat that might have been overlooked during the skinning process. After that, the furs were hung up on nails in the basement to dry. That would take several days, during which the hides would become hard and paper-like. The pelts were then removed from the boards and stacked up, to be taken and sold to the Buckhorn Fur Company or another fur buyer. The musk smell of the furs permeated the whole basement. That odor was not welcomed upstairs by our mother, so we always made sure to close the basement door when we went back upstairs.

The whole trapping idea was just too gruesome for some members of the family, so they didn't get involved in it. I think that they just didn't grasp that there was something between Dad and the animals, something that even those of us who shared it with him didn't quite understand.

We learned a lot about nature and about life out there on the trap line. I know that we will never forget the times we had and the things that we did together.

Casey

Several years ago in the springtime, Dad and I were talking on the phone. It was planting season and we had so much to talk about that I planted four flower beds while holding the phone between my shoulder and my ear. We must have talked for more than an hour.

I told Dad that he should see my flower beds. I told him he could learn something from me. He laughed and said, "Yeah, sure, but I know that mine are nicer. There is not much you could teach your dear old dad about growing flowers." I told him that I would take pictures and send them to him and prove that my flower beds were nicer than his. He said, "OK, you just do that."

A few weeks passed and we talked almost every day. We were always comparing the kinds of flowers we were setting out. One day he asked me what happened to those pictures that I had promised to send him. I explained that I had been waiting until my flowers got a little bigger so that the pictures would really show their beauty. He just laughed and said that I probably didn't even have any flowers and that I was just making it up.

That statement sent me straight to the store for film. I came back and took pictures of anything and everything that I had growing. I took the film right down and got it developed. I put the pictures in the mail the next morning.

A few days later, the phone rang early one morning. I picked it up and it was Dad on the other end. He said, "Hey, guess what I got in the mail today?"

"I don't know Dad, what did you get in the mail?" I had a pretty good idea.

He said, "Someone cut these pictures of flower beds out of a magazine and sent them to me. You don't know who would have done a thing like that, do you?"

I told Dad, "Don't even try it. Those are my flower beds and you know it." After kidding me for what seemed a long time, he told me that my flowers were so beautiful that they could be in a magazine. That made me feel so proud.

About a week later I got a letter in the mail from Dad. I opened it only to find pictures of beautiful flower beds, cut from magazines. I ran into the house as fast as I could and called him right away. When he answered the phone, I was laughing so hard that I could hardly talk. I finally said, "Come on, Dad, those are not your flower beds." He tried his best to convince me that they were, and then I reminded him that I grew up there and knew every square inch of the yard. He gave in.

When Dad died in March, we brought him home for his wake. It was a Saturday morning and all the family, including his sister, Frances, was there. We were sitting around telling stories about him and going through his photo albums. As we looked at the snapshots he had saved of all of us, we came across the pictures that I had sent him of my flower beds. A piece of notepaper was stuffed in the album beside the pictures. Dad, being the jokester that he was, had written a caption on the paper. It said, "Raised by a recruit up in River Falls."

I guess he got the last laugh after all.

CHAPTER TWENTY-SEVEN

A Life's Work

DACE HAD VARIOUS occupations during his lifetime. He started out as a house mover with his father and brothers. That work often included laying blocks for basement walls and pouring cement floors. It also involved some carpenter work, so he developed many of the basic skills of building construction.

Later he became a cement finisher, working on the new highway between Fennimore and Boscobel. He learned form-setting and road-building along with curb, gutter, and sidewalk construction. He loved working outside in the fresh air. Dace was once asked to become a salesman in a store but he refused, saying that he wouldn't be able to stand being inside all the time.

For a while, he worked at the local Borden's plant. This was inside work, and although he didn't like it, it brought in a regular paycheck for his growing family. The job was a blessing because it came at a time when there was very little building or road construction going on.

Later he worked for the City of Boscobel, at the sewage treatment plant. At first, the job seemed to him to be the lowest form of work that a man could do, until a local doctor told him that he had the health of the community in his hands. After that he began to take more pride in his work and studied the science of his job.

He was fascinated by the fact that a sewer plant is a living organism. The raw sewage enters the plant and goes through a process of being oxygenated in a series of open vats. After an initial breaking down of the material, it is pumped into a digester where fermentation occurs as the helpful bacteria work on the sludge, as it is then called.

He was surprised to learn that this process has similarities to both bread-making and wine-making. The digester had to be kept at a certain temperature so that the anaerobic bacteria would have just the right conditions to perform their function.

Protecting the bacteria so that they stay alive was time-consuming and required a detailed knowledge of what he was doing. This meant that he must further his education. He took basic microbiology and chemistry courses through the University of Wisconsin Extension program and advanced math courses by correspondence. In his time at the plant, he did a considerable amount of scientific measuring and monitoring in the laboratory.

Despite the knowledge and expertise required to do this job successfully, Dace never received proper appreciation or recognition. To those who didn't know better, he was just a man who worked at the sewer plant. Any fulfillment he received in his work came from the knowledge that he was protecting not only the public health but his beloved river and its fish, as well as the river bottoms and swamps and the wildlife they supported.

His operation of the plant was constantly monitored by the State of Wisconsin. Not only the city health department but the Wisconsin Department of Natural Resources surveyed the plant on a regular basis. Dace was always proud that his readings were within normal range and often above normal. The effluent was as clear as spring water, and fish below the plant were plentiful, so he knew that the plant was performing well.

Operating the sewer plant was a full-time but low-paying position that lacked status. The city administrators had no knowledge or appreciation of his job, nor did the public itself. It was at this point that he felt that some education of the public was in order. He talked to the grade school and high school science and chemistry teachers and scheduled plant tours for the students so that he could explain the operation.

He was disappointed after giving his first tour, the students giggling and holding their noses through his explanation. After that, he went to the school before the actual tour and told the class what to expect, and explained that the sewer plant was an actual living and breathing being, much like an animal. He talked to them about aerobic and anaerobic bacteria. He explained about pathogens and helpful bacteria and how they hurt us or help us in our everyday lives. He showed them how he did some of the tests and explained why he did them. Only then would he take them through the plant, showing them how everything worked and demonstrating the tests.

The attitude of the students changed completely once he prepared them for the tour beforehand. They were fascinated and almost in awe of the digester. The laboratory was a complete surprise to them. They loved all the flowers he had grown from sludge, and they showed an interest in the fertilizer beds and the clear effluent that came from the plant. What a transformation it was from the influent that came into the plant from the other side! They let him know how much they appreciated what he was trying to do to protect them, and to protect the environment.

I guess he felt that this generation would at least appreciate the importance of this kind of work and how vital it was to the community and to nature.

Dace was the only person in town at that time who had any knowledge of the plant, since the city administrators didn't feel that the cost of training a backup person was justified. The old man who had taught Dace some of its operations had been there for so many years that the city just never became aware of what was involved in his job. All they knew was that, when something smelled bad, the state would get on their backs to get the place running properly.

Since he didn't have any help, he was on call 24 hours a day, 7 days a week, 365 days of the year. He couldn't even take a vacation the first six years he held the job, because there wasn't anyone to substitute for him. Members of his own family sometimes substituted so that he could have a break.

Eventually, the shoddy treatment he received from the city began to affect him so deeply that his family encouraged him to return to cement work. He was spending so much time alone being unappreciated that he began showing some serious signs of alcoholism. It would be years before he would get full control of the illness.

After his experience with the city, he worked for a local contractor for a few years and then went into business for himself. He had always hoped that he would one day own and operate his own small concrete construction company, and this was his chance.

By then he had become a relatively good carpenter. As a result, building homes was added to the many other trades that he had taught himself. He found a great deal of satisfaction in the work and eventually was able to forget about his past troubles with the city.

Dace was a born teacher. Being in business for himself meant that now he could teach his children the skills that he had acquired over the years.

The six boys and three girls in the family worked with their dad from time to time, building cement steps and patios or pouring basement and garage floors. They became fairly good at it, too. Every one of them could run the power trowel or work a bull float. They knew a good magnesium trowel from a poor one and could use an edger like a pro. They learned to set and care for forms and knew when a job called for a five-bag mix or required a different strength of concrete. Dace was always so happy when he was able to discuss the details of a job with them and know that they understood what he was talking about.

During his later years he worked as a custodian for the state and retired from that job following heart problems. His heart condition improved but he developed leukemia. Even that didn't keep him from working.

His last job was a part-time position with the Boscobel schools doing maintenance repair work and lawn care. He enjoyed the activity of the school and loved talking to the staff and the students.

One day, he injured his hip while getting off a tractor after mowing the school grounds. He was taken to the Veterans Administration Hospital in Madison and underwent hip surgery. An infection soon developed, and since his immune system was impaired as a result of leukemia, his general condition deteriorated very rapidly. He lost more than a hundred pounds over three months.

When Dace realized that he would not live much longer, he asked his medical team to release him from the hospital so that he could go home to Boscobel. There he could be with his family and friends and spend his remaining days in the place where he had so many memories of happier times.

His doctors agreed with his decision. Late one evening he left the hospital for the long ambulance ride home.

CHAPTER TWENTY EIGHT

The Return

DACE WAS THE seventh and last child born into his family. He was baptized and confirmed in the Immaculate Conception Catholic Church in Boscobel and was graduated with the first class of students who went all the way through the new Catholic grade school that was built in 1937. After grade school he attended Boscobel High School and was graduated with the class of 1948.

When our children started to school, he insisted that they go to Catholic school. As a result, he and the nine children received a combined eighty years of education from the small school.

Dace was very conservative when it came to his religion. When the changes in the Mass came in the sixties and the Mass was said in English instead of Latin, the change was very hard on him. He drifted away from his religion for some time, which saddened him greatly in his later years. He attempted to modernize his thinking and even attended some charismatic services that were associated with the Church, but it was useless. For some reason he felt the changes left him out, so he stopped going to church altogether. Strangely enough, however, he continued to insist that the children go to church regularly and to the Catholic school.

It was during this period that his life took on many problems. The grief over the loss of Francine who died so suddenly affected him spiritually, and the disappointment of being unappreciated by the city fathers in his work seemed to devastate him.

The assassination of President John F. Kennedy and Dr. Martin Luther King and Bobby Kennedy along with the onset and continuation of the Vietnam War certainly contributed to a general feeling of helplessness that he experienced. After the death of his mother in the late sixties, and then the untimely death of Peter in a car accident in 1976, his drinking problems worsened and at times he seemed all but lost.

During this long, dark period of his life, he stopped going fishing and hunting and doing any of the things that had brought him so much happiness during his earlier years.

Two of the few stabilizing forces in his life at this very low point were his special love for the Blessed Virgin Mary of the Immaculate Conception and his increasing interest in working on my family's land in the country. Strangely enough, these two forces would eventually work together to pull him back from the abyss of total darkness.

We had heard that a Catholic school in Prairie du Chien which had been closed for several years might have some slate blackboards that could be bought for a small price. We went down to Prairie du Chien and met with the priest at St. Gabriel's rectory. He gave us the keys to the school and told us that we could go over and look around and see if there was anything we could use.

That was when we found the statue of the Immaculate Conception. She was life-size and standing with a piece of plywood against her face with the slate blackboards leaning against the plywood. We were shocked to see this. Since the changes in the Church and the removal of many of the statues had become the vogue, many priceless works of art were lost or destroyed. We removed the slate and the plywood and discovered a beautiful statue that was sculpted in Italian marble. The priest gave us the statue after learning that we wanted it for a shrine out on the land.

We immediately went home to Boscobel and got help to move the statue. We put our good innerspring mattress in the back of an old GMC van and returned to Prairie du Chien. It took six men to lift the statue onto the innerspring mattress so that it could be safely moved. When we got to the land we placed the statue in a secluded area close to the road, where the trees formed an umbrella over Her head.

Dace took a special interest in the statue and the surroundings. He raked away all the debris and planted flowers all around Mary's feet. He made ornate cement benches and put them in the little garden so that people could come and sit and enjoy the solitude. He arranged it so that the water in the spring on the small hill above the shrine came down a pipe and splashed on the rocks near the flowers at the feet of Mary.

When he rested from his work in the fields, he would come and sit on one of the benches and eat his lunch and plan how he should build an arch over the statue to protect it from the elements.

We had learned from the priest that had given us the statue that it originally stood outside at Campion College and had been placed there when the college was first built. He said that it had been brought to the

United States from Italy and had been commissioned to be sculpted especially for the school. He believed it to be a statue meant to be placed outside and that after the school had been closed and the property sold, the statue had been brought to St. Gabriels and stored there.

About the time the statue came to our land, Dace recovered from his drinking problems and never again even had a desire to drink. The family never attributed his recovery to anything to do with the statue, but his attitude toward the changes in the Church were different. Something inside him had changed, and in time he became more like his old self. He started going back to church and was instrumental in helping others recover from similar problems. He never did think it was right to take communion in his hand, however, so I guess he didn't give up all of his old thinking.

Dace discovered that Fr. John Urban was looking for a statue of the Immaculate Conception for the church. In all the years since the church was built, it had never had a statue for the namesake of the church. He took Father John to the land to see the statue, and came to believe that the father appreciated this wonderful work of art as much as he did.

The statue had eroded considerably. Acid rain and the years of being exposed to the elements had stripped away the protective shield that covered the stone. It would have to be restored. The statue was taken to Gary Krause, a professional stone mason in Viroqua. He meticulously worked on it with loving care over the next three years, working on it a little at a time when he was free. The work was finally completed in early December of 1998 and the statue was brought home to Boscobel and placed in the vestibule of the Immaculate Conception Church just in time for the Solemnity of the Immaculate Conception on December 8th. What a miracle that was! The statue returned home where She belonged on that very day!

During that same three-year period, there was a marked deterioration in Dace's health. His leukemia had worsened and in September of 1998 he developed an infection that could not be cured. He entered Veteran's Hospital in Madison and, with the exception of a short time in November, he remained there until late in December.

When it became apparent to him that he would not get better, he requested that the medical team permit him to go home to die. They agreed, and arrangements were made to transfer him to the family home in Boscobel. He had become so feeble that his doctors thought that the trip might be too much for him and that he might die en route.

His only request before going home for the last time was that he wanted to see the statue again. He wanted to see Her where She belonged, at home in the Immaculate Conception Church.

The members of the Boscobel Rescue Squad were aware of his request, so when they transferred him they stopped at the church and backed up to the door. Family and friends were waiting as they took him out of the ambulance on a stretcher and wheeled him into the vestibule of the church.

Fr. Urban was there and gave him a blessing. Tears came to his eyes as he reached out and touched the hand of the Holy Mother.

The three friends, together again, for a brief moment! The priest, the man, and the statue.

Then they took Dace home to die.

River Cycle

Robin Chamberlain Transo

Sand molds
cast with warm body strokes.
Clenched hand;
dripping slurry towers and castle walls.
She leans back under dragon clouds,
to watch sun races over the river hills.

The hawk circles her head in winds
that kiss warm breezes over her face.
Her father rides on those winds she feels;
his spirit drifts here over the ancient river
like the smell of willow bark and river sand.

Here, no other place exists.
Currents rope islands to pull them to distant shores.
She sits a lifetime;
watching the changing river remain the same.

Across years;
footprints increase upon the sand,
castle walls long since give away to reflections
of the eagle cliffs above still backwaters.

Cutgrass on unsuspecting legs,
as small willows grow almost beyond hugs.
The wind blows up a small dried turtle shell;
leaving another story a sand mold.

Eulogy

James Chamberlain III

The hunter has gone home to his hills,
   the sailor has found rest on his sea
and we gathered here shall not see
   his like again
So, in contenting ourselves with memories,
   imperfect reminders of what once was,
we sadden ourselves over time wasted
   and lament times never to be.

For we shall not see his like again.
   His shoes ne'er to be filled,
not to walk these hills again,
   to tread the trails unmarked paths
known only to the few by sign and sight,
   and sound and smell.

Man and animal this day to gather round
   together marking this man's passage
to his hills,
   his streams and forests
each of us marking this moment in time
   as if it were our last.

Now in our hearts
   his face before us now,
that graying beard
   age grayed and winter winds tossed.
That fixed and focused gaze
   discerning in the forest
the creation of life
   and the damage of man.
In his arms he holds his life's tools,
   to build with the permanence of stone

to shape wood
    with deftness and beauty,
to hunt with peace
    and a respect for life.

This day the beasts too do him honor,
    for though they know they may live longer
they may not die with such respect.
    And they see that his life was as short as their own.
For he was in every sense nature's best,
    a man at peace in nature's home,
at comfort in the earth's presence.

A man now at rest,
    whose spirit ne'er to be troubled by tiredness,
his gait ne'er again to be slowed by a year's weight.
He shall walk and wander these hills and streams
    long past the echo of my poor words.

And when we see the work of less talented men
    we will always say that we have seen better.
And upon our faces we will smile
    remembering his hands at work
shaping and finishing,
    molding and mastering
with steel and sweat,
    with laughter and an Olympian appetite for life
and we will be humbled to say we may live longer
    but certainly not better.

So we gather here today,
    for we shall not see his like again
nor his boots easily filled.
    For his visit is over
and he has returned to his earth
    leaving us fragile and humbled at nature's workings.
For the hunter has returned to the hills,
    and the sailor is at rest on his sea.

-end-

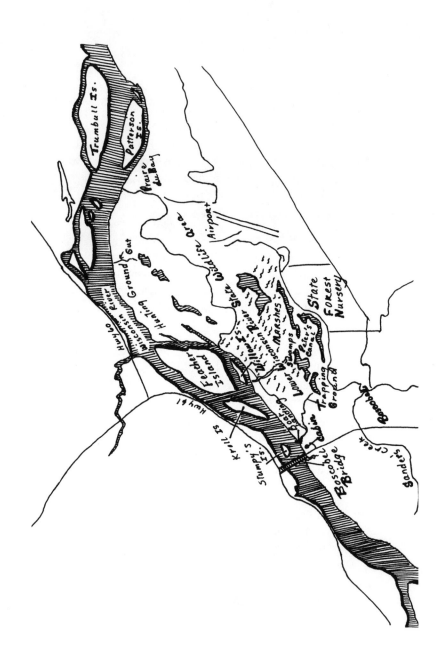